# Transform
## W

*Practical Strategies to Inspire*

*Sustainable Change*

Margaret Stockley RN, CWPC, CWC, RYT

Alva Glen Press

# Other Books By The Author

*Inner Knowledge:*
*Harnessing the Senses for Peace, Balance, and Health*
(with Lorrie Jacobsohn)

Transforming Workplace Wellness
Practical Strategies to Inspire Sustainable Change

Copyright © 2016 by Margaret Stockley
All Rights reserved.
Published by Alva Glen Press
ISBN 978-0-9969825-0-4

Cover Design by DanJac Design

*Thank you to Cliff*
*for always being a bright light.*

# Contents

## PART I: The Wellness Perspective

# PART II: Strategies For Managing The Wellness Program

# PART III: Resources

# Introduction

Congratulations! Whether you are about to embark on creating a wellness program in your company or are seeking ideas on how to transform or invigorate an existing program, you have a great opportunity to transform the lives of your colleagues, and in some cases their families. As a change agent, you are charged with developing a wellness strategy and delivering actions that inspire, engage and reach beyond the various interventions that are established to initiate behavior-change. What a wonderful position to have; helping individuals to reach personal goals and achieve healthy behaviors that will stay with them for a lifetime, while shaping the culture of your company.

The Center for Disease Control (CDC) estimated in 2012 that nearly 50 percent of adults were living with a chronic disease such as diabetes, heart disease, stroke, arthritis, or cancer, with 25 percent living with two or more conditions. This is costing billions of dollars in healthcare costs; e.g. the total costs of heart disease and stroke in 2010 were estimated to be $193.4 billion for direct medical costs, not including the costs of nursing home care. Chronic disease is a critical problem associated with unhealthy behaviors that can be changed. In 2014, almost 120 million people were employed full-time in the US with an additional 7.5 million part-time workers out of almost 319 million people living in the US. The CDC states that four of these health risk behaviors; lack of exercise or physical activity, poor nutrition, tobacco use, and excessive alcohol use are the main causes of illness, suffering, and early death related to chronic diseases and conditions.

Corporate wellness programs continue to grow and evolve as more is understood about employee and employer needs in the workplace, the motivational factors that encompass participation, and what to do with the accumulation of data on health and wellbeing. This growth is fluid and ever evolving and shaped as much by the types of programs offered as by the response and feedback of employees and the information gathered from the evaluation of programs.

The reasons for having a wellness program are multi-fold, and ensuring that employees are rewarded for a job well done, have a sense of purpose, are involved in decision-making, and are happy and motivated, are all major factors in talent management and retention as the time and costs in hiring and training a new employee can be as high as 30 percent of an employee's salary. Putting the focus on employee health status management can minimize the effectiveness of programs and as you read this book you will see that it returns the emphasis to wellness, in all its forms, and to help drive individuals, organizations, communities, and ultimately the country to be more healthy, energetic, and productive.

While your own organization will have its own motives for implementing a wellness program, the common drivers amongst companies are:

1. Health care costs
2. Retention
3. Talent acquisition
4. Engagement
5. Health and safety
6. Competitiveness

One size does not fit all when it comes to wellness programming and the aim of *Transforming Workplace Wellness* is to equip the wellness team with the foundational knowledge to build and develop their own wellness program. The traditional method of wellness programming focused primarily on health risk assessments and providing information on problem areas such as smoking, obesity, and lack of exercise. In *Transforming Workplace Wellness,* the approach is holistic, encompassing a broad outlook that takes into consideration movement, nutrition, and tobacco cessation programs as well as stress management, financial needs, meditation, social and community involvement, and even spirituality. This well-rounded approach is effective because it spreads beyond the workplace highlighting the connection between the workplace, home, social life, and the community. Life is not played out in a vacuum and it is the wellness program managers who are creative in their methodology that are successful in combining winning content with engaging events.

The results of a one-year study published by Steven Nyce et al, in the November 2012 edition of the Journal of Occupational and Environmental Medicine, 54(11): 1364 – 1373, *Association Between Changes in Health Risk Status and Changes in Future Health Care Costs: A Multiemployer Study,* sought to examine the relationship between health risks and health plan costs in over 22,000 employees. They found that identified health risks increased the annual health plan cost by an average of $210 per year and each year forward. Conversely, if a health risk factor were reduced (of those types examined) it reduced the average annual health plan cost by $129 per year and in each year forward. They concluded that keeping "low risk" individuals from acquiring health risk factors was a more economically efficient way to minimize future health care costs.

It is not enough to simply offer programs or incentives in order to improve healthy behaviors. Studies continue to demonstrate the correlation between the effectiveness of implementing successful wellness programs with a positive Return On Investment (ROI) and increasingly a positive Value On Investment (VOI). Each of the steps in this book will help you in building an effective program that is designed to meet the requirements of your organization and corporate culture. For ease of understanding, throughout this book a wellness program refers to the main wellness program, beneath which there are sub sets of programs, such as a stress management program, and beneath this program are interventions such as yoga or meditation.

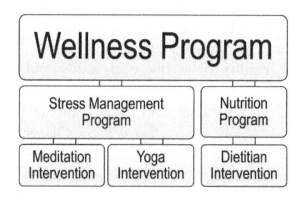

You will learn more about building a plan and connecting it with the wellness vision and corporate culture in chapter two. The program vision, VOI, and anticipated benefits are the foundation of the program and the program's performance will be measured against them. Since 2011, there has been a strong shift towards VOI elements such as engagement, impacting business performance metrics, improving employee job satisfaction, and positively affecting presenteeism.

A Harvard University study of 100 peer-reviewed journal articles, *Workplace Wellness Programs can Generate Savings*, found that "medical costs fall by about $3.27 for every dollar spent on wellness programs and that absenteeism costs fall by about $2.73 for every dollar spent." The authors concluded "employer-based wellness initiatives may not only improve health, but may also result in substantial savings over even short-run horizons."

Wellness programs vary in cost and can range from $50 to $500 per person annually, depending on the types of programs offered and the expected results. Your program model will ultimately drive the costs, depending on whether your organization simply wants to have some feel-good events such as walking programs or weekly lunches where the whole department sits down for a company sponsored lunch, or whether there is a thrust towards a results-driven program where biometric levels are monitored and change-behavior programs are implemented. Health, wellness, and wellbeing components are broad in their potential applications and while "knowledge of wellness data is power," when it comes to being proactive in the choices of programs to implement and being alert to the ones that work and don't work for your organization, ultimately it is the type of programs offered that are important in effecting lasting change, rather than an emphasis on data analysis. Analysis and evaluation are important however, and each of the steps in this book provides you with the foundational information that you will need to use in order to take the information that you acquire from the early analysis and surveys and build programs that are engaging, informative and ultimately help employees transform their behavior. The execution of the many dimensions of wellness will in turn create not only healthy employees but also a healthy organization reflected in changes to policies, a productive and constructive culture, and by management embracing their active role in conveying a positive message of caring about their employees' wellbeing.

This is where a well-structured wellness plan can make an impact, as your interventions create lasting change that not only benefit the employees, but also produce a wave of positivity that permeates throughout the company, the local community, the state, and eventually the nation as a whole. *Transforming Workplace Wellness* is a systematic approach incorporating seven steps that are essential to building and executing a wellness program that works. Each step is designed to help you identify and achieve your specific organizational wellness goals by utilizing a layered approach that flows through all levels of the organization. The rewards for an organization choosing to run a wellness program are well documented and include financial benefits, increased retention, and improved morale. The advantages are lengthy and woven through each chapter as each area is discussed in detail. Now we will take a closer look at how to integrate the seven steps with the latest evidence-based research and create your own unique and flexible program.

**Overview Of A Corporate Wellness Program**

A wellness program is not only an investment in the employees, providing them with the tools to recognize their personal health and fitness needs and the skills to make behavioral changes, it is a structured approach tailored to the needs of your company, reinforcing organizational policies and strengthening the goals and vision set forth by the executive management team while driving down health costs. Ultimately, self-motivated action aids in creating more engaged employees who, in the long-term, can utilize the tools provided, either individually or as part of a team or group, thereby allowing the wellness team to manage the program efficiently and proactively, and offer services that are meaningful, enjoyable, interesting, and varied. The components of the wellness program need to align with the strategic structure of the wellness plan and incorporate tactical and operational elements.

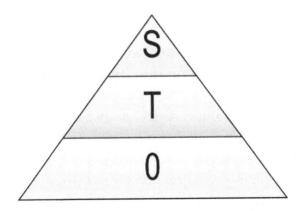

- Strategic: Program design, policy decisions, goals, objectives
- Tactical: How to achieve the plan, program planning
- Operational: Day-to-day decisions, program execution and monitoring

Your wellness program will include short and long-term strategies to foster engagement, provide interventions that are stand-alone or run for several months or even years, and put standards in place to evaluate results. Popular programs are explored in-depth in chapter four along with the types of policies and evaluations that should accompany them. Flexibility in the types of programs that you offer is key, with additional activities added depending on the demographics and needs of your employees, e.g. annual breast or prostate screenings, stress management, or financial wellness management. These will be evidence-based strategies to motivate and engage employees, engender accountability, and identify and track at-risk behavior based on information from employee and organizational needs, screenings, health risk assessments (HRA's), and research studies. With a tailored platform, programs can be offered to all employees including non-office based employees and employees on assignment who will also have an opportunity to explore, participate, and reap the benefits, thereby cultivating a corporate culture of shared values. As a change agent, you will tie in the vision for the wellness program with the company culture, with employees and management, and learn how to inspire lasting positive change through teamwork, communication, and accountability.

When building a program it is imperative that it is in compliance with state and national regulations such as the HIPAA security rule. This area requires careful monitoring to ensure that the program does not fall short in meeting the latest government directives and is discussed more fully in chapter seven. Your wellness plan will therefore contain policies and procedures to safeguard the company and all employees, include protective measures to ensure confidentiality, comply with health and safety initiatives, and embrace best practices to deliver a program that meets the highest possible standards. This advice can come from a variety of sources such as your benefits provider, insurance broker, human resources department, and legal department.

The most fundamental goal of a wellness program is to provide activities that lead to actual positive changes in health behavior. In 2012, approximately 150 million Americans received healthcare through their employer and with costs continuing to rise employers are tending to shift some of the responsibility of payments to their employees. It makes sense therefore, for both the employer and the employee to create a working environment that promotes health, rather than solely focusing on decreasing actual costs, or worse, limiting access to healthcare.

A joint consensus statement from organizations including the Health Enhancement Research Organization, American College of Occupational and Environmental Medicine, American Cancer Society, American Diabetes Society, and American Heart Society states that "it makes practical sense for employers to play a positive role in influencing the health behaviors of their workforce." They further state that worksite wellness programs also make sense from a public health perspective because:

1. Most people spend a majority of their day at work.
2. Worksite factors (e.g. group processes, policies, environmental resources) can support individuals in changing health behaviors.
3. Family members can also be reached.

An evidence-based program will craft and meld evolving trends such as health/life coaching and work-life balance initiatives with a clear wellness vision that is designed to align program results with business metrics. Preventive actions that are measured, evaluated, and flow with the changing requirements and events that occur in life mean happier and healthier employees, fewer demands on existing benefits offered, reduced overall costs, and an increased revenue potential for the organization.

While promoting life-style changes and education, a structured yet flexible wellness platform also highlights the role of the employee in taking responsibility for their own wellbeing while providing tools to influence employees and assist them in seeking out ways to change habits, one at a time. This is achieved through an environment that reinforces healthy options and surrounds employees in a culture that values their health and makes it easy to engage in healthy activities.

**Shifting The Culture**

One of the effects of implementing a wellness program, other than positive changes to an individual's health or reduced benefits costs, is the impact that it has on the culture of a company. If there is no shift in the culture, subsequent programming will struggle to succeed, wasting money, time, and morale. Each step in creating your organization's wellness program, plus each program that you introduce, will ultimately play a role in transforming both personnel and departments and will therefore need to be integrated progressively in order to introduce the programming effectively and smoothly into the organization. People by nature fall into habits and routines and change is not always easy. The interplay between employees' expectations and the organizational drivers affect the sustainability of a business and the retention and morale of staff. Wellness programming does not typically represent sudden change, however the announcement of the introduction of such programming can affect an individual's perception of themselves, their expectations, and level of job security. Thorough and frequent communication of the wellness message will go a long way in alleviating any concerns, rumors, and create a cohesive environment for the program to thrive.

For example, in order to make it possible for employees to train for a half or full marathon, a policy may need to be created to support flexi-time along with subsequent training and preparedness of managers so that they understand both the new environment and how to apply the new guidelines in order to ensure that employees know that they can make use of such a policy without repercussions. This deliberate move to embracing change in the corporate culture conveys a clear message to the employees that the company genuinely cares about work-life balance and their health and wellbeing. This shift in culture is necessary in order for employees to feel comfortable and confident enough to participate in and engage in the program.

A flexible wellness platform allows all programs to be customizable based on the vision and needs of the company and the pre-programming information. Feedback from direct managers, HR, and face-to-face interactions by designated wellness team members can also generate great ideas around activities and ongoing support during the information gathering stage and later on in the evaluation stage after an intervention has been completed. They can also be a useful resource in managing change and the resulting shift in culture. Maintaining flexibility within the planning stages and during each wellness event, or intervention, is important as requirements evolve, regulations are updated, and additional information is received. If the wellness plan is too rigid, it can result in low participation, low engagement, and poor results.

Prior to the 1970's, a healthy company was deemed to be one that was free from physical or chemical hazards and complied with OSHA standards. Research was beginning to consider the interactions between an individual's motivation and their performance as a means of determining their effectiveness and potential. According to research conducted by the University of Cincinnati Industrial and Manufacturing Engineering Program in 2004, in the early 1990's productivity versus health and safety was being blended to reflect "organizational health." Additionally, Williams (1994) identified four elements of organizational health: environmental factors, physical health, mental (psychological) health, and social health reflecting a more holistic approach to health in the workplace. As you move forward with designing your wellness program, these particular characteristics of organizational health will also reflect and complement the types of interventions that are relevant for the employees, once the appropriate data has been obtained and employee surveys completed.

Communication is a central feature in helping people to understand the reasons for the wellness programming, managing the resulting changes towards policies and the environment, and maintaining a positive attitude to what is happening. Creativity, originality, and spontaneity go a long way in designing programs that best suit the employees' interests, producing ideas for programs that are packed with fun and exciting strategies to make a lasting difference. The benefits of a structured wellness program for both the company and the individual are shown in the following table:

| COMPANY | INDIVIDUAL |
|---|---|
| A reduction in health costs | Reduced out-of-pocket costs |
| Time off work | Impacts employee paycheck |
| Creating a healthier, happier, and informed workforce | Optimizing employee well-being |
| Higher staff retention and improved morale | Increased satisfaction at work |
| Demonstrating commitment to meeting the needs of the employees | Would recommend their workplace to friends and associates as a great place to work |
| Progressive community leadership | Enhanced job performance |
| Less absenteeism and increased productivity | Knowledge of personal biometric levels |
| An engaged workforce, a recruitment tool | Lasting behavior change |

**Wellness Program Cycle**

While each company is different in terms of demographics, culture, and industry, there are seven key steps, shown here, that are the foundation of every successful wellness program:

1. **TEAMWORK.** A coalition of leadership and the organization working together to develop an inspiring health and wellness vision and a strategy for achieving it.
2. **SHARED VISION.** Identify and embrace a common purpose, needs, and goals to sustain transformational change. Communicate the vision through shared aspirations.
3. **WELLNESS PLAN.** Defining the plan and developing a wellness brand.
4. **CULTURE.** Supporting sustainable change through empowerment and engagement.
5. **GENERATE WINS.** Recognize contributions and celebrate victories.
6. **DEVELOPMENT.** Increase the circle of influence to shape and grow the best elements of the program. Create a spirit of community.
7. **EVALUATION.** Evaluating programs and managing the process of change. "This is the way we do things around here."

14

You will learn about each step of a wellness program cycle in detail in this and subsequent chapters, honing and fine-tuning every phase to fit and grow within your company's culture and meet the goals that you determine are best for the company and employees. The programs that thrive are the ones that make it personal for the participants and use the basic coaching methods of identifying real needs, i.e. motivating factors, and providing the means to create small, sustainable changes.

# PART I: The Wellness Perspective

# CHAPTER 1

## Step One: Teamwork

*A Coalition Of Leadership And The Organization Working Together To Develop An Inspiring Health And Wellness Vision And A Strategy For Achieving It.*

Executive sponsorship is key during the whole process of a wellness program, from their vocal and physical support in the strategic planning phase to the ongoing development of the program. One or two senior executives will be members of the wellness team and therefore required to commit their time and resources while actively endorsing and fostering ongoing support for all aspects of the program.

Their role is important on several fronts:

- Communicating their belief in the value of the program
- Providing and approving resources for events and initiatives
- Approving new policies related to the wellness program
- Enforcing accountability
- As a visible participant in programs in order to improve their own level of health
- Helping to build the wellness team

Additionally, if an executive sponsor competes in sports they may consider a role as one of the wellness champions, leading and encouraging others to participate in a sport as well as join in program events.

An article in the December 2010 issue of The Harvard Business Review (HBR) listed what they call *"The Pillars of an Effective Workplace Wellness Program."* The HBR visited ten organizations with financially sound wellness programs and they found that these organizations had six strong pillars that could be adopted by other companies who desired to achieve positive results within their own organization. The first pillar was Multilevel Leadership where wellness was "passionate, persistent, and persuasive".

Your company's dynamic is unique and the wellness program's initial success hinges on the support of executive management. And remember, in addition to their position in the program, executive management will also expect to see a solid wellness plan, receive regular updates on its progress, and obtain reports on evaluations that demonstrate that the program is successful.

### Establishing A Wellness Team

Forming a team and leading them in a successful wellness program is an exciting prospect and one where it is important to bring people onboard for their skills and enthusiasm as well as any specific knowledge or experience that they may have. This can include current certification in a fitness discipline such as yoga or coaching, or proficiency in successfully training for and completing races. Furthermore, a broad array of professional talents and abilities allows for access to specialized knowledge and other expert resources, as the wellness program is not a separate stand-alone initiative but rather another facet of your company's culture that integrates with the existing values while contributing to future goals.

If the size of your company is large with over 1,000 employees and perhaps multi-site facilities or employees who work remotely, you may wish to consider forming a wellness team consisting of a principal team that can include up to ten representatives from different departments, such as HR, Benefits, IT, Finance, and the Catering Team who will all meet both regularly or when needed for a particular event, and a smaller sub-set comprising the planning team who will meet weekly and focus on overseeing the planning and implementation of the program.

On average, a mid-sized company of 200 to 1000 or more employees will require around four to six team members and the length of time from planning the wellness program to initiating interventions may be considerably less than that of a larger organization, but this is dependent upon multiple factors including the decision-making process, existing resources, and the ability to acquire and analyze data.

## Team Responsibilities And Talents

What are the responsibilities and talents of the wellness team? Teams are typically assembled based on subject-matter skills and the wellness team is no different. Their overall enthusiasm for wellness is vital in driving the strategy and momentum of the program, however selecting employees with the right balance of abilities is also important. These essential elements include having experience in a broad spectrum of professional and vocational specialties such as project management, marketing, accounting, leadership, analysis, legal expertise, IT and vendor negotiation. The composition of the team's skills and demographics should therefore be as broad as possible, not just including employees who may already be participating in healthy lunch or walking groups, or those who are known to participate in sporting competitions.

The members of the wellness team are change agents and should also represent a percentage of the various demographics of the population or employment that your organization encompasses i.e. the percentage of men to women, salaried or hourly paid, younger and older employees, and if there is a trade union or other organizations that should be consulted regarding inclusion in the formation of the wellness team. Additionally, their skills should be broad and varied.

As we explore each step in building a wellness program, you will see that success is more than a team effort; it is a company-wide effort. The appointed team members can complete allocated tasks independently or use the resources within their department, including seeking assistance from colleagues for their ideas and opinions. Working as a team also means that there will be times when a team member will be required to reach out to other members of a department within the company, yet outside of the wellness team, for additional support or information. Don't forget to send an email to the respective department, stressing the importance of the task and thanking them for their help. Remember that communication in all its forms has an essential role in successfully transitioning through change.

Appointment to the team should be viewed as recognition and an opportunity to increase skills. The HR department can assist you in identifying potential members for the team by helping you to determine the people who represent the prerequisite demographics and who have the knowledge base and enthusiasm to help build the structure of the wellness program. Wellness is a long-term commitment and the wellness team will be in place for the duration of the program, therefore it is advisable for large teams that members be rotated every two to three years with new members overlapping as outgoing members complete their term. As before, each future member of the team will be selected for their expertise and ideas along with their passion and energy.

**Wellness Champions**

In addition to specific skills the team will include one or more wellness champions who bring a high level of enthusiasm for the program in general. Wellness champions are core members of the wellness team who have the specific role of being champions of the program, rather than champions of fitness, and it is their willingness to embrace and express their confidence in the benefits of having a wellness program that engenders ongoing interest and enthusiasm by their colleagues as the program evolves. These individuals should be people who consider themselves enthusiastic about the various aspects of health and wellness, come from any department with any level of authority, and may either act solely as ambassadors for the program or also contribute their departmental skills to the team. Wellness champions should report to the program manager.

This is a role where it is vital that the correct personnel are put in place. Wellness champions are often well-liked or respected and are of particular use in the early weeks of the launch of the program, and prior to the introduction of new interventions and programs. As a result, they will frequently be tasked with promoting the interventions within their own departments, or other groups if it is a smaller organization, encouraging co-workers to sign up for events and generating excitement for all aspects of the wellness program.

The role of the wellness champion is at a tactical/operational level and with the ability to influence other employees in the organization, the wellness team should consider the specifics of the role and the function of the champion in detail. They should decide whether the wellness champion is to be seen solely as an ambassador, or whether there will be a promotional role to their position. Additionally, wellness champions will frequently be working in the program at a grass-roots level and can provide fabulous insight on what it is like to be an actual participant as well as offer detailed feedback that will be of great help to the team when planning future sessions and interventions.

Your champions need to be recruited carefully to ensure that they are willing to volunteer for individual and/or team events, be involved for at least one year, and have a solid grasp of the importance of confidentiality as this is a visible role and their actions can either help or hinder the program. The position should be advertised within the organization and the candidates interviewed by HR and the program manager with the executive sponsor giving final approval and announcing the appointment. This, as you can imagine, gives credence and importance to this role that can be both ambassadorial and operational too!

Gather the names of all people who are interested or who may be a suitable candidate to be a wellness champion. The top champions are those with a passion for the program, for fitness or a goal, and are known for their positive outlook. They are also enthusiastic, see great benefit in the program, and want to involve others. If they are to be formal members of the wellness team, or members-at-large, they will need to be given an actual role, with their responsibilities clearly defined, along with the corresponding reporting and fiscal responsibilities.

Reporting is two-fold. Each champion will be required to provide feedback on the intervention as a whole and offer feedback to other wellness champions on what they have encountered. The role of a wellness champion may be a new initiative and any other champions in your organization will be eager for actual hands-on information and lessons learned.

Ultimately, wellness champions are also change agents for the program and can help you immensely. By default, you are also a wellness champion, however you should not be the only one!

## EXAMPLES OF A WELLNESS TEAM SKILLS-SET

| DEPARTMENT | SKILLS |
|---|---|
| Executive | Final decision-making, authorization, endorsement, and |

| | |
|---|---|
| | approval of resource requests. |
| HR | Knowledge of compliance, health and safety, insurance, demographic knowledge. |
| Benefits | Sourcing free resources from vendors. Benefits knowledge and ability to explain changes. |
| Marketing | Branding and promotion of wellness message. |
| Catering | Ability to make healthier food and meal choices. |
| Finance | Budgeting and ROI calculation. |
| IT | Deliver health messages using intranet and apps. Data protection. |
| Wellness Champion | Supports the wellness initiative. From any department and level of authority. Is a campaigner and advocate. |

**Confidentiality**

This area covers multiple topics that will prepare the wellness team for conducting surveys, organizing programs, and staying current with trends in corporate wellness. There are various ways that confidentiality can be protected, from ensuring that there are no identifiers when gathering information during surveys or when reviewing your company's demographic material to ensuring that documents and databases are secure.

Confidentiality is a responsibility of both the wellness team and the company in relation to compliance with the current legal requirements surrounding privacy and health and protection of the information.

Data breaches are costly to companies and your IT department can work to ensure that safeguards are in place to protect the data and to minimize the number of people who have access as a viewer, reviewer, and a creator. How to gather information and other forms of research is discussed in depth in the following chapter. However, the need to handle confidential data sensitively and perceptively underlines why it is crucial to consider very carefully who the prospective wellness team members will be and interview them to ensure that those who are brought onboard understand the importance of being in compliance with confidentiality at all times.

Participants of the various wellness programs may either intentionally confide or inadvertently share their private information to members of the wellness team, including wellness champions, thereby putting all team members in the position of being privy to personal health information. The Human Resource department is often the best department to provide training and education on how to manage the sensitive subject of confidentiality, the law, and the consequences of violating the Health Insurance Portability and Accountability Act (HIPAA) Security Rule. Further information and guidance material on HIPAA can be found at the website of United States Department of Health and Human Services.

**The Role of The Wellness Program Manager**

This is a position that can garner a lot of attention from management and other employees and the executive sponsor will typically select the person most suitable for this role. If you are fortunate to have been given responsibility for managing the team, which can range from a dedicated/full-time team to a matrix/part-time team, you will be tasked with assisting with recruitment, investing in building the team identity, and nurturing the dynamics of relationships with each member as well as overseeing the various wellness programs.

The wellness team will be managed and supervised in the same manner that any other team in your organization is managed. Getting to know the team early will be especially useful when the time comes in the future to resolve any disputes, find replacements, and perform evaluations. The program manager will not only oversee the events and programs, but will also:

- Lead the team in defining the aim and purpose of the program
- Have an extensive understanding of how different factors and projects will affect and steer the flow of the program such as the culture of the organization
- Coordinate the timeline of the program
- Discover the needs of the company and employees
- Determine the demographics and identify suitable wellness interventions

An organization's structure, culture, and style affect how projects are managed along with the triple constraints of scope, time, and cost. If either one of these changes, it affects the other two. The program manager should be visible and clearly show that they are following the five phases of a project: initiating, planning, executing, monitoring, and closing. These phases apply to each of the wellness program steps and to individual events and interventions. Visibility enables the program manager to monitor all progress, manage the team, and ensures that people know who is in charge.

Make it easy for people in the team and the organization to come to you with ideas as well as concerns. This is especially useful once programs are up and running and an effective way to observe established programs is by talking to participants.

Be approachable!

In addition to managing all of these aspects, executive management will rely on the program manager to not only be familiar with the company culture, the management style, and establishing the best options for communication within the wellness team and the employees but will also require evaluation reports as the overall wellness program progresses, whitepapers on the benefits and return on investment, and of course be able to deliver a plan that will ensure that the program is a success.

Each step of the wellness program infrastructure will create a solid foundation to build the wellness activities upon and obtain measurements for evaluations as well as continuous improvement. Ideally they should be used in the suggested order in this book, as it will be a challenge to proceed with developing a program if, for example, you have done research and have a team selected only to find out that the CEO is not on board or that financially the organization has chosen to redirect resources in a different direction.

Teamwork is very much in play when you are developing the wellness plan and putting structures in place. If your organization is small to mid-sized it will be easier to find the information that you require to create or evaluate as the individuals managing the departments such as HR, Benefits, or even the health plan provider will often have direct access to the data. A multi-site organization poses a different challenge and you may need to go through multiple chains of command, complete data request forms, or simply be persistent in calling the person responsible in the respective department until you acquire the data that you need. You can see that maintaining professional working relationships is a desirable key skill of each team member and especially so in this situation where both the role and the program may be new, are highly visible, and will require the program manager to be in contact with multiple individuals from different departments and across multiple disciplines.

Additionally, wellness team members also need to be motivated in order to stay enthused, interested, and excited about what their wellness mission is all about. Motivation and engagement are discussed throughout the book and its important role in engaging employees. As with any team, recognition for a job well done is important and this applies to both individual achievements and the group effort of completing goals.

Be generous in this area!

Give rewards where they are due and celebrate when milestones are achieved, especially when the initial project is complete and the wellness program is officially launched. Do let other employees know about successes along the way and the progress made to date. This generates additional interest and excitement around new or revised programs that are coming soon.

Being a part of the wellness team is a multi-faceted role and employees will soon get to know the names of the team members via a variety of communication methods that are highlighted later in the book. With a motivating, rather than penalizing, wellness program, employees will be eager to share their success stories with team members, whether it is to show how well they placed in a race or the small changes they have made to their daily diet.

Now isn't that a rewarding job!

## Scheduling The Meetings

The scheduling of meetings and other communications need to align with the S.T.O. structure mentioned earlier and will be more frequent in the early planning stages, accompanied by the inevitable challenge in bringing everyone together. However, visible support by senior leadership goes a long way in reinforcing the importance of the program.

The first wellness team meeting assumes that various decisions have already been made, such as:

- Executives have decided to launch a wellness program
- The program manager has been appointed
- The strategy and goals have been decided
- The budget has been assigned
- The core team has been selected

In the planning and information gathering stages the early meetings for the wellness team should be at least bi-weekly, requiring more frequent sessions in the run-up to program launches. The senior executive who has authorized the mandate to proceed with the program should also be invited to attend the meetings because of the significant importance their visibility in mentoring the program brings to the program as a whole.

The role of the program manager in coordinating meetings may also include chairing a sub-committee, if the size of your organization warrants one. The sub-committee will consist of a core group of around five people, depending on the scope of the program, who will collate and analyze data submitted to them and prepare the material to be presented at the subsequent meeting of the whole team.

The first wellness team meeting sets the precedence for future meetings, giving attendees an opportunity to express ideas and formulate tasks to complete by the next meeting in order to drive the project forward. It will cover a lot of ground and lay the foundation of the overall wellness program. Tasks include:

- Deciding where the meeting will be held
- Ensuring it has the necessary equipment and seating
- Distributing the agenda to team members at least four weeks and thereafter 24-48 hours in advance

Exploratory research and preparation needs to be conducted prior to attending the first meeting and it is useful to add the names of presenters against the topics that will be discussed in the agenda. The planning stage will take several months and team members will need to see regular progress, be motivated and encouraged, and feel valued for their contributions. The style of meetings should be open, energetic, and can be varied, for example, held outdoors or the sharing of a positive health or fitness update from team members to demonstrate that wellness is not just being talked about, it is being put into action.

**The First Agenda In Detail**

Attendees are members of the wellness team and the first meeting will set the professional tone, interest, and character of subsequent gatherings as well as propel the ongoing enthusiasm for the new wellness program initiative. The group that assembles at the first meeting will include, at a minimum, the executive sponsor, the appointed program manager, and representatives from the HR and Benefits departments. There is a lot of material to cover in the early stages including determining the additional members of the wellness team, defining the mission statement, creating a timeline, and establishing the goals of the program. However, by adopting a crawl, walk, and run approach more elements will be incorporated in an efficient timescale with a controllable, on-budget program as the end result.

## 1. Introduction of wellness team members

Team members will take turns to introduce themselves with their title and department and mention any health or fitness skills (e.g. yoga certification or participation in sports competitions) and their specific reason for participating in the wellness program. The reasons may range from a general interest in fitness to the sharing of a specific personal goal that they want to achieve. This should take no more than one minutes per person, less if there is a large group. If necessary, have a business contact list of name, title, department, email, and business phone number to email to team members.

## 2. Mission statement for the wellness program

The executive sponsor and senior leaders who either initiated or approved the program should have a clear idea as to what they want the overall program to achieve. They have given permission to start the project with authorization to spend money, dedicate resources, and begin the development of the wellness program. The program manager MUST have this permission in writing.

Preparing a mission statement will be one of the first tasks that the wellness team will do and the statement will define the values that will distinguish the program and what it desires to achieve. It is a concise statement that can be referred to at numerous times to ensure that each wellness initiative is on track with the overall vision and guide the team with selecting interventions that are within the confines of the mission. It also helps with identifying the goals and purpose of having a wellness program.

**Example of a mission statement**

"The mission of the Wellness Team is to support employees in making healthy choices and maintain a workplace and environment that supports healthy lifestyle choices."

### 3. Identify goals and benefits to the company

Now that you have the go-ahead for the project, the specific goals that must be achieved need to be identified. As mentioned previously, programming costs can vary considerably and the return on investment for your company will depend on the program model that you choose (described in detail in chapter four) to the additional resources that you use, such as paying the salary for a dedicated wellness consultant, using financial incentives, all the way to building an in-house gym. You can see that there is a broad scope for costs that are incurred, which is why there is no one-size-fits-all approach to wellness programming. Prior to the first team meeting, the finance department will be able to provide the senior executives with an indication of the resources available for investing in the program. The Finance department can provide an overview of current healthcare costs and the Benefits department can provide the projected return on investment based on examples of wellness programs at companies similar in size and productivity as your own. Sources of where to find wellness studies are located in the resources section at the end of the book.

Without knowledge of the financial data, statistics, and related information it is hard for management to make an informed decision and give the go-ahead for the program, however at this early stage, further research and documentation will need to be completed by other members of the wellness team in order to know which programs to strategically put in place and determine what the targeted outcomes should be. Again, this depends on information such as demographics, is your organization mostly male or female, results of employee needs-based surveys, all the way to the logistics of reaching shift workers and off-site workers such as a sales force.

As the planning for the wellness program develops and is eventually implemented, the vision for the program along with the associated company values and benefits will be measured and evaluated against actual performance and results. Is the program meeting the value on investment objectives? Is the program giving an agreed minimum return on investment? This area is explored further in chapter two.

### 4. Any questions and scheduling the next meeting

Aim for consensus at each discussion point on the agenda. Define the actions and next steps, and set clearly defined goals. Remember to thank attendees at the end of each meeting and ensure that everyone knows their tasks and the date, time and place of the next meeting.

### What To Include In Subsequent Agendas

As the program develops, more questions will be raised, more data will be required, and eventually more information will become known. A timeline will be required to define the activities, show the sequence and required inputs, the estimated duration of activities, record the resources required to complete each task, and enter the scheduled dates for the estimated completion of the activities. The wellness team should be aware of what will need to be included in it and factor this in when developing programs and interventions. The Project Management Institute outlines three elements of a timeline as comprising of inputs, the tools and techniques, and the outputs. They further state that there will be constraints built into the timeline due to mandatory, discretionary, and external dependencies.

**Mandatory dependencies** are fixed and therefore cannot be altered or started until another activity has been completed. This is often referred to as hard logic. An example of a mandatory dependency (hard logic) is the type of building that your organization is located in. It could be a large campus or it could be a series of offices on a floor in which other companies are located. The building and its location are therefore fixed, as they cannot be changed.

**Discretionary dependencies,** on the other hand, are soft logic where the wellness team, for example, makes the decision to choose to start one activity rather than another based on their expertise, knowledge, and even known best practices.

**External dependencies** are items that are outside the control of the wellness team. For example, a program may start on time or be delayed through the prompt or late delivery of items from an external third party.

Knowledge of each of these dependencies will also allow for building in leads or lags in the time-management of launching the program and subsequent events by accelerating or delaying an activity. The timeline will expand as the program develops and as more information is known about needs and goals, the sequencing of events and resources will be applied to control the workflow. You can choose how you share this information; as a diagram or even a spreadsheet, however all updates should be documented and all changes tracked.

This accrued knowledge will drive future agendas and will typically incorporate and address the following topics:

1. Introduction by the program manager with their perspective of the progress and any issues identified
2. Current wellness plan status
3. Updates on events/interventions
4. Functional updates
5. Special topics such as insurance and state compliance
6. Update on company policies
7. Accomplishments for the next meeting

**Examples of future tasks**

1. Initial data collection and evaluation
2. Identify needs and benefits of the employees (survey of employees)
3. How communication will be managed
4. Branding the program
5. Building a website for the wellness program
6. Utilizing wellness champions
7. Budgeting
8. Defining the wellness operating plan and scope of the program
9. Initiation of a Work Breakdown Structure (WBS)

10. Identifying community and regional resources to access
11. IT to disseminate information and promotion of programs
12. Defining programs and events
13. Incentives
14. Building the wellness environment
15. Benefits updates that may impact events
16. Yearly calendar of planned events
17. Program evaluation methods and frequency
18. Establishing Return On Investment and Value on Investment

**An Enthusiastic Team**

As progress reports are made and achievements shared at each meeting, the roles of team members will be further defined providing opportunities to connect deeper with the purpose of the program. In many companies, members of the wellness team continue with their principal role, such as working in HR or the Benefits department, while also working in a wellness capacity. Typically, it is only very large organizations that can have wellness personnel working in the position full-time. All employees, including the team members regardless or whether they are working in a wellness capacity full or part-time, are on a journey to health and wellbeing, each with their own goals and motivating factors. Successful programs have several traits in common including a dedicated and passionate team, a flexible plan that meets the needs of employees and the goals of the organization, and is committed for the long-term. Creating meaningful ways for the team to remain engaged will foster innovative ideas, renewed interest, and an invigorated partnership with colleagues as they work through the planning stages and the subsequent phases of ongoing development in order to create wellness with and for the employees.

Following the first meeting of the wellness team, the various members will be busy working on their assigned tasks. With the first timeline plan ready to go, the program manager can now start overseeing the progress and ensure that gathering the needs-based information related to the employees and the company starts on time.

## Review Checklist

1. Identify the executive sponsor
2. Assemble the wellness team
3. Recruit the wellness champions
4. Define the roles and scope of wellness team members
5. Establish a vision and goals
6. Define and approve a mission statement
7. Outline an initial wellness plan
8. Create a timeline

# CHAPTER 2

## Step Two: Shared Vision

*Identify And Embrace A Common Purpose, Needs, And Goals To Sustain Transformational Change. Communicate The Vision Through Shared Aspirations.*

Successful programs are not standalone events; rather they connect the core wellness strategy with the company culture. Wellness is a far-reaching goal encompassing visible executive sponsorship and the gathering and utilization of information to develop personalized programs around a shared vision. Determining the requirements of the program entails defining wellness, as it pertains to your organization, while keeping the definition broad enough to allow for the integration of new knowledge and resources. This involves adopting a comprehensive yet flexible approach that unites the common purpose of the program with employee and organizational needs and goals.

The corporate health and wellness profession continues to evolve through the increasing knowledge contained within the numerous clinical studies, research papers, surveys, analysis, best practices and evaluations that are published annually. In order to gauge the parameters and types of programs that you will offer, it's important to understand what you know about your employees and what they know about the organization. This will assist you in defining programs that fit in with the business strategy, including any community role that is either currently in existence or is desired to be included in future programming.

A 2010 report by the Center for Studying Health System Change analyzed information from industry experts and employers sponsoring wellness programs and determined that one-size-fits-all programs purchased from vendors were ineffectual. They concluded that wellness programs needed to be comprehensive, diversified, and customized to the individual organization.

Your overall wellness program therefore must have a strong plan and strategy, offer programs that address identified needs, be easily integrated into the existing culture, and be flexible enough to grow and develop as attitudes and mindsets evolve. That is no mean feat! How do you incorporate this knowledge into your own program?

Gathering information to develop programs around a shared vision will not only uncover a precise baseline to facilitate future evaluations of the program and measure progress, but will typically expose information that is not currently known thus providing the wellness team with the opportunity to adopt a proactive and customized approach to wellness. It will require multiple surveys combined with an evidence-based method of analysis to understand the wellness strategies that you will need to put in place. This enables the wellness team to refine the wellness plan, hone the interventions that will be offered to employees, provide a tailored approach to wellness, and ultimately develop holistic programs that will address the emotional, physical, and financial needs of the employees while meeting the goals of the company. Furthermore, this approach also allows executive management to formulate better decisions around the direction that they wish the program to go in and the amount of resources they want to allocate.

The wellness team will want to utilize the expertise of other team members for example the HR, benefits, and finance departments to construct the surveys and assessments that will involve interacting with the employees at all levels, such as shift-workers, full or part-time employees, and those who work out of the office, such as a sales force. Incorporating different viewpoints and attitudes is particularly useful in not only constructing appropriate methods for research, but in having the right people in place to analyze the information and build the most suitable programs based on the acquired data. Some of the initial areas to focus on include:

**Employees:**
- Demographics
- Employee needs
- At-risk behavior
- Presenteeism and absenteeism
- Chronic illnesses
- Injuries and disabilities
- Biometric screening
- Stress factors

**Employers:**
- Types of benefits provided
- Actual health care costs
- Community partnership
- Resources
- Holistic approach

In addition to gathering the internal organizational and employee demographic information, the wellness team can also gather data from the healthcare provider, government organizations, research papers, and even during wellness fairs and conferences. The benefits and finance departments should work to provide data on the company's healthcare and benefits costs, track the costs of providing wellness events, the internal and external technology factors, and eventually compare the impact of wellness interventions to determine which ones are contributing to creating a healthier employee base or resulting in lower premiums. In addition, associations with vendors and benefits providers must be cultivated as they can supply you with facts, statistics, and even resources.

This is the baseline that the wellness team will use and moving forward there may be opportunities to tighten certain areas, or offer different benefits packages. Future projections can also be made to estimate costs and other needs as the wellness program grows and moves towards increased participation. A quarterly review of the data will demonstrate that the wellness program is on track to meet its objectives and the shared vision.

When considering what to include in your program, you may want to move beyond traditional biometric analysis and embrace a holistic approach that includes financial health and emotional wellbeing. The majority of your employees are not typically in the extreme risk category so it is vital that you approach wellness from different angles such as looking at the ages of your employees and determining the other issues that are affecting them and their health. Millennials for example will often have different social and emotional needs than someone who has children in college and/or aging parents.

What does health mean to your organization?

What policies do you need to put in place?

How will you inspire engagement?

When thinking about these questions, employ a strategic approach towards fostering shared aspirations by leveraging the information to build a solid framework that promotes and sustains transformational change. Utilize other departments for assistance with research or statistics as required. This further highlights the need to cultivate and maintain solid working relationships with co-workers and identify who is responsible within your own organization for providing additional information that you may need.

**HIPAA**

The Health Insurance Portability and Accountability Act of 1996 (HIPAA) is federal legislation that was created to protect consumers' health information. It set rules in four areas: transactions and code sets, identifiers, privacy, and security. The US Department of Health and Human Services (HHS) provides an overview of the key elements that organizations and individuals should be aware of including how to safeguard electronic protected health information. Importantly, it is the responsibility of each employee who handles health information to be aware of the policies and practices associated with security and patient privacy. The consequences of not complying with the rules can result in penalties for both the organization and the individuals involved. At the time of publication of this book, the HHS current rules regarding the Health Information Technology for Economic and Clinical Health (HITECH) Act, states the following:

---

Section 13410(d) of the HITECH Act, which became effective on February 18, 2009, revised section 1176(a) of the Social Security Act (the Act) by establishing:
- Four categories of violations that reflect increasing levels of culpability;
- Four corresponding tiers of penalty amounts that significantly increase the minimum penalty amount for each violation; and
- A maximum penalty amount of $1.5 million for all violations of an identical provision.
HITECH Act 2009

---

The HR department should formally instruct the wellness team members regarding the measures they need to take to ensure that they comply with all aspects related to the HIPAA rule and to the company policies governing confidentiality. Additionally, team members should be provided with training on the steps they need to take to avoid inadvertently discovering specific information regarding an employee's health and how to handle any confidential information or sensitive material that may in fact be shared directly to them by an employee.

Information that is obtained during surveys or any other source should not contain any identifiers. Likewise, the team should be updated regularly on the laws around health disclosure and the types of questions that cannot be asked during the information-gathering phase. These are not just best practices, they are the law in regard to privacy and HIPPA regulations and the strict guidelines apply to everyone, to safeguard the rights of the individual and also prevent litigation. As you can see, there are numerous categories of data that you will want to acquire in order to determine the unique requirements for your organization, your employees, and your community.

**Employee Data**

Acquiring this data is two-fold and involves obtaining information directly from employees using a variety of mediums and researching in-house material related to employee demographics. Involving employees from an early phase conveys the level of commitment by the company to the health of their employees. Applying generic data can work for constructing one-off programs that are fun and informative. For example, holding an exploratory day with a variety of complementary health practitioners, such as a hypnotherapist, a naturopathic physician, or an acupuncturist who demonstrate what typically happens during a session using one or two employees as volunteers. However generic data is not typically used for long-term programs where positive behavior changes are expected, such as weight loss. Generally speaking, employees are not fans of the "pry, poke, or prod" type of analysis, often disguised as a wellness program. These are not in the real spirit of wellness programs, and while they have their place in data acquisition, they do little, if anything, to positively affect lifestyle habits or promote healthier behavior.

Establishing and quantifying the specific needs that are unique to your organization highlights the issues that are important to your employees, including the concerns they are currently facing both at work and in their personal lives. This information provides a foundation for communicating the shared wellness vision, while helping to identify what may be the best initial programs to implement. Your choice of programs in turn provide a framework for evaluating and gauging progress and making amendments and improvements to the overall program on an agreed timescale.

There are a variety of employee specific surveys that can be used to help you make informed decisions regarding the type of programs to introduce:

- Surveys targeted at specific employee demographics e.g. to men only
- Confidential (anonymous) interest-based survey
- Conducting a confidential HRA (Health Risk Assessment)

These can be obtained from your state, health insurance company, or purchased from an outside vendor and are useful in large organizations. **Note:** the information obtained from HRA's is completely confidential with no identifiers and only aggregated information is provided to the employer such as the percentage of men to women, or the percentage of employees who do not exercise.

HR is one of the best suited departments to complete the detailed task of employee demographics as they have access to information such as the percentage of male to females, the spread of age groups, any language constraints that may impact promotional material, how many are field or shift-workers, are there any disability needs, and any known family responsibilities if dependents are being included in the wellness program (without specifically naming anyone). Legally, wellness programming MUST be open to ALL employees and the more information that is known about the requirements of employees, the easier it is to fine-tune aspects of the program to improve engagement and participation. An example of the relevance of this type of information, at a basic level, is that men and women would be offered screening information relevant to their gender.

A confidential (anonymous) survey will typically ask questions to discover employees' wellness and fitness interests, if work impacts their family life or health and vice-versa, and these types of questions will help the formation of a wellness plan that provides the topics and events that employees want to participate in. It can be conducted on-line and the types of questions asked will strive to capture the needs of the individual based on their gender, age, and activities. All opinions and feedback can further define the shared vision and tailoring of the program and it is best practice to outsource the survey to further emphasize the confidential nature of the information. Targeted surveys that explore a wide range of needs and subjects are a useful tool in assisting the wellness team to design multicomponent programs that address areas related to productivity and health and help employees identify and work towards achieving their specific health goals.

Use an online survey from a company such as Qualtrics, Survey Monkey, or Constant Contact.

- Tailor the questions to suit the demographics and needs of your organization.

- Ensure that you inform the employees that all responses are anonymous.
- Use questions that are unbiased, unambiguous, have a wide range of choice, and ask one question at a time.

**Response ranges include:**

- Very Interested, Somewhat Interested, Not Interested.
- Strongly Agree, Agree, Neither Agree Nor Disagree, Disagree, Strongly Disagree.
- Extremely Likely, Somewhat Likely, Unlikely.

**Demographics:**

Ensure that the age range is appropriate for your organization and that there is a wide representation of both sexes to avoid any possible identification of respondents. For example:

- Male, Female
- Age Group: Under 35, 36-45, 46-55, 56-65, 66 and older. (Alter the range to suit your organization.)

Sample questions and templates for a wide variety of surveys and evaluations are included in the Appendix section.

Personalizing the programs is made further possible by understanding where individuals are on their readiness to change from one period of time to another, and by intertwining strategies with the ever-changing social and personal conditions that everyone experiences during their life.

## Small Groups

While much of the data gathering will be done through the analysis of personnel statistics or anonymous surveys, personal interface in small focus groups is a great way to get to know employees and establish a relationship with them as well as building a strong evidence base for your programming. These small group sessions can be conducted in person or via conference calls, depending on the size and location of departments within your organization, and can discuss a variety of areas including personal interests, an events wish list, lifestyle and activities, or any useful skills such as certification in yoga that may, for example, be incorporated in future programs.

However, it is also an opportunity for employees to ask questions of you, to find out more about what is expected of them, and the reasoning behind the decision to have certain interventions. Cultivating a supportive culture and environment throughout the company is a critical factor in fostering a successful program. The informal sharing of opinions should also help you formulate thought-provoking questions to direct to the wellness team such as:

- How does the corporate culture affect the choice of program?
- What aspects of the corporate environment need to change in order to be more conducive to employees' needs and the ever-shifting social culture?
- What can we change corporately to create a more conducive culture that supports employees and their needs?

Wellness needs are not only medical needs; they are the events that impact the "sandwich" generation who have teens/college-age children as well as elderly parents who are reliant on them; they are the people who are dealing with marital issues, or individuals dealing with a catastrophic life event such as a cancer diagnosis in the family. We all have pressures on us and while you may not know what an individual is dealing with in their everyday life, the very simple action of "keeping a door open" and being accessible goes a long way in conveying the message that the company cares and is there to offer the assistance that they need. Ultimately, meeting in person (within a small group) is more than a useful tool for helping with early participation and engagement; it is a way of staying truly connected.

**Health Screenings**

Health screenings are often run in conjunction with an HRA and examine baseline parameters such as lifestyle choices, exercise, sleep, blood pressure, cholesterol, glucose, and body mass index. The findings are highly confidential and an outside agency such as the healthcare provider or an independent company should manage the screenings. The results will only be shared with the employee who should be encouraged to discuss the findings with their primary care physician if there is a health concern, as this information may be new to the employee and even indicate a serious illness.

Your organization also needs to prepare itself for the reality that screenings may in fact uncover underlying health concerns and consider how this will impact planning, budgeting, and future interventions.

The total results for the company will then be collated, any identifiers removed, and the general statistics provided. This may yield information such as 30 percent of employees are smokers, 45 percent are overweight, and 10 percent have type 2 diabetes. The reasons for certain health conditions may not be known but the collective data will help you to establish a baseline of aggregated employee health conditions, health risks, and any associated costs.

You can see how this will help you with honing the details of the wellness plan and future programming, however it also shows you the number of employees who DON'T have significant health concerns. This has important implications because it lets you know the number of healthy employees that come to work every day and invites you to consider the impact this will have on the future programs and incentives that you will offer in order to motivate and engage these employees.

## Broad Picture

Gathering the various materials surrounding your organization's policies, values and requirements, financial readiness, corporate culture, workplace environment, and demographic information and interests of employees is no mean feat however they are crucial in helping you to build a solid foundation for the wellness program. In addition, data can also be obtained from your healthcare provider, government organizations, research papers, and even wellness fairs and conferences.

By now, you may also have decided if the wellness program is for employees only or if the families of employees are to be included in the program too. Statistically, including partners and families improves the likelihood of the wellness program being a success so a small upfront cost can reap higher rewards through engagement, motivation, satisfaction, as well as a healthier workforce and lower benefits premiums.

As mentioned earlier, the employees and the company are the two focal areas for gathering data to establish both needs and a shared vision. The wellness team are also responsible for conducting all research related to obtaining statistics, feedback, and evaluations. Consider what must to be added or modified to the existing infrastructure:

Do additional policies need to be in place?

Do best practices exist for specific programs?

Will additional resources need to be added to make a program viable?

There may already be a list of questions that you know you want to ask, however the results from initial surveys may also highlight additional areas where questions may need to be asked in order to seek clarification or fine-tune an aspect of the plan.

**Types Of Company Research:**
- What is the current best practice to implement new policies? How easy is it to implement new health and wellness policies?
- What is the data on health insurance claims, workers compensation, and drug costs?
- Environmental. What needs to be changed to better promote wellness and what already exists to facilitate wellness programs e.g. an on-site gym or nearby walking trails.
- What is the company insurance liability for intervention programs?
- Catering and vending choices. For example, what vending choices exist? What are the costs of using organic products in the cafeteria?

- Are there any smoking cessation or weight loss programs already in place?
- Are there any established yoga programs or walking groups?
- Do any employees have licensed skills or coaching certifications they can use in programs?
- Community. What role and impact does the organization have in the community through volunteering and as a role model for wellness?

The assimilated information will assist the wellness team in building a wellness-operating plan that is wide-ranging and provides a baseline that allows further monitoring of the program's progress. All information gathered throughout the life of the wellness program should have a consistent layout and must be securely filed, accessible, and contain the names and professional details of employees involved in running the surveys and obtaining information.

The Centers for Disease Control and Prevention provides a basic checklist of assessments that you may wish to consider utilizing as you research interests, costs, and how best to structure your wellness plan and programming.

Success is in the details.

Each of the seven steps of the wellness plan will require gathering, assessing, recommending, analyzing, and comparing of data at various stages throughout the life of the program. This level of thoroughness will also ensure that the opinions and responses of employees are heard and the overall program is tweaked to reflect additional knowledge.

## Establishing The Wellness Plan Objectives And Goals

There are few events in life that can succeed without planning and goal setting. In the workplace, the process of planning and working towards a shared wellness vision creates a strong foundation to build the program upon. Additionally, you will integrate feedback from the executive leaders regarding their corporate vision for the program, the parameters to be included, and what budget they are willing to allocate. There is no guesswork associated with planning and the demographics and needs-based surveys will support the action to determine the requisite interventions and whether they will take place on site or in the field, depending on the spread of the workforce. Remember, ALL employees should have access to interventions regardless of their place of work, i.e. field, factory, shop floor, or office.

When thinking about planning, consider what resources, people, skills, and strengths are available to the team. This will help you in directing your efforts into formulating goals to reach the desired outcome for the wellness program and each intervention. The International Coaching Federation lists planning and goal setting as one of the core competencies and the mnemonic S.M.A.R.T. made popular by George T. Doran in the November 1981 issue of Management Review, is used to assist with the process.

- **S**pecific - What specific goals need to be achieved
- **M**easurable - quantify how to identify when success is attained
- **A**ssignable (or actions) Who will do it and/or what actions will be done to achieve the goals

- Realistic - achievable goals based on available resources
- Time-related – specify when each result will be achieved

Examples of S.M.A.R.T. goals are provided later in this chapter. Doran also expressed that it is the combination of the objective and its action plan that is really important. The purpose of setting specific goals is to frame the information into a documented step-by-step approach that acts as a motivator to the wellness team that the operating plan is working and that they are on track to launching a great wellness program. This is significant not only for planning and setting goals for the wellness program, but also when formulating goals for the interventions and events that will take place each year. Goal setting for interventions and the planning of the events is explained in detail in chapter four.

**The High-Performing Wellness Plan**

Now that you have a good understanding of the company and employees, there are additional factors that will be incorporated into the wellness plan. Typically, these include an environmental assessment, aggregated employee data, HRA's, environmental safety, disability and workers compensation, and medical and pharmaceutical claims. This data will establish a baseline not only for defining policies, but for the program purpose and direction too.

The process of strategic planning provides direction as to the types of programming to offer based on what has been identified as needing to be achieved and the available resources. Of course, not every need will be met in the first year, however by prioritizing each of the combined organizational needs and identified health risks, a year-on-year plan can be started and the ongoing flow of the wellness plan determined:

- What are the factors to aim for in the first year?
- What percentage number do you need to increase an activity to?
- Will the program be more aligned to reducing pharmacy costs by x percent?
- What lifestyle choices do you need to decrease and by what percentage?

Use the known shared objectives to create meaningful programs that will bring about positive lifestyle changes by combining elements of both. This means offering comprehensive programs for healthy employees, who typically are the majority of your employees, as well as those who need to eliminate a detrimental habit or make healthier choices. A program can, for example, have different levels of achievement and rewards to motivate and create ongoing interest and participation. A clear purpose will guide the program direction and the strategy to build popular support, to educate and to effect policy change while helping to meld the wellness program brand with the company culture.

Best practices research shows that the focus is not solely on policy change or offering incentives to change a health behavior. There are other success criteria that are at the heart of a well-designed program including:

- Modifications to policies to support organizational, environmental, benefits design, and healthy culture changes. These are responsible for increasing employee engagement in healthy behaviors and health improvement.

- Societal issues such as offering opportunities to volunteer. This has consistently been shown to motivate employees and help them feel good about belonging to their organization.
- Local resources that can be tapped into: walking trails, discounted gym membership.
- Redesign of benefits coverage.
- Financial wellness coverage.
- Intrinsic and extrinsic motivation comprising motivation, action, and outcome.
- 24-hour access to a nurse hotline.
- Environmental and physical work area considerations.
- Creation of a wellness mission statement by executive leadership and visible involvement in all aspects of the program.
- Incorporating cutting-edge research to build evidence-based best practices into the wellness programs.
- Recruiting and on-boarding of new hires.

These elements are geared towards enhancing the operating plan and personalizing the program to make it meaningful to employees. The goals and purpose of a high-performing wellness program have far-reaching consequences beyond one-off events and interventions.

A 2007 study in the American Journal of Health Promotion *"Impact of a Health Promotion Program on Employee Health Risks and Work Productivity"* examined three areas:

1. The cumulative count of health risk factors and the World Health Organization health and work performance questionnaire
2. Workplace absenteeism

3.  Work performance

The results demonstrated not only a positive ROI, but also significantly reduced health risk factors and monthly absenteeism while increasing the work performance scale.

Careful planning combined with acquiring and utilizing the right information will therefore provide a solid foundation for your own successful wellness program; one that incorporates a holistic approach to wellness and infuses a strong sense of shared responsibility between the employees and the organization. Well-designed programs vary in their scope and implementation, however they all invest in the employees and meet organizational requirements.

**Funding And Resources**

In order to calculate how much to allocate to the wellness budget for items such as interventions, screenings, additional personnel, and renting or buying equipment you will need to factor in both the cost of administering the programs as well as the incurred benefits costs triggered by employee life-style behaviors. Additional stand-alone projects e.g. an on-site gym or clinic would be calculated and planned as a separate endeavor due to the complexity of such a large project. However, data-driven analysis will enable you to develop protocols, policies, and best practices that will drive initiatives and determine how much the actual costs will differ from the expected costs.

The *Employer Health Benefits - Annual Survey by The Kaiser Family Foundation* provides detailed information on employer-sponsored healthcare including premiums, employee contributions, cost-sharing provisions and employee opinions. The 2015 report showed that the annual premiums for employer-sponsored health insurance were $6,251 for single coverage and $17,545 for family coverage. This demonstrated a 4 percent increase over 2014. Also, between 2010 and 2015 premiums increased by 27 percent and by the same amount between 2005 and 2010 compared to 69 percent between 2000 and 2005. The report further reported that since 2010, deductibles for all workers have risen almost three times as fast as premiums and about seven times as fast as wages and inflation.

Cost analysis therefore has to be both qualitative and quantitative, utilizing a variety of sources including state and national statistics that can further assist you in determining the resources that you need to allocate to your programs. Combined with your earlier data-gathering tools that highlighted employees' preferences, demographics, and organizational needs you can also formulate a baseline of existing medical cost levels.

Determine what is currently spent on healthcare, resources, and what percentage of the operating costs will be allocated to the wellness program. Approval for the budget should be obtained in writing from the executive sponsor. This is in addition to the earlier mention in chapter one regarding obtaining approval for initiating the program.

**NOTE**: The program manager MUST obtain approval for every step.

Many of the events and interventions in *Transforming Workplace Wellness* are free or low cost, and if your company does not have a training/education department there are surveys and other tools available that are free to use or inexpensive to purchase, plus doing most of the planning and development in-house also saves on costs. These are listed in chapter eight.

An additional range of resources, brochures, and possible discounts are available from benefits providers and the Health Enhancement Research Organization (HERO) as well as associations such as the American Cancer Society, the American Diabetes Association, and the American Heart Association. Check with your local state for additional resources, including funding for programs, and also any federal allowances that are available. There are specific rules and regulations that organizations need to adhere to when running a wellness program to ensure that it is HIPAA compliant, offers incentives that are suitable to all employees, discloses the availability of alternatives in all communications and program materials, and continues to meet regulations. Typically, these rules are updated annually so it is to your advantage to know what is available to you and what alterations you need to do to ensure compliance. Sponsored incentives from benefits providers include rebates or discounts of membership premiums at health clubs, or participation in health promotion, or disease prevention programs.

Determining the impact of interventions on employees' health, morale, and productivity is necessary too as it's not enough to provide a service that sounds good if there is low uptake or the results do not justify the expense. Cost benefit is not only monetary; it is also the soft return of increased motivation, employees recommending the company or its products to their friends, or perceiving the organization as a great place to work.

The economic cost of events will impact the overall program as well as determine if an intervention is effective in reducing previously incurred costs, or if monetary incentives are literally paying off. However cost benefit analysis is a separate issue from that of costs incurred in running a program and is discussed in chapter seven.

## Recruiting And Onboarding

The building and implementation of the wellness plan should not only focus on the numerous aspects of health and wellbeing that will be covered in future programs, but also extend to talent management. Both the hiring process and the onboarding experience are perfect opportunities to expose new hires to the wellness culture and introduce them to the variety of health and wellness programs available. The excitement of starting a new job frequently carries over into the programming, encouraging new recruits to sign up and participate. Statistically, engaged and motivated employees are more productive while the company who offers wellness programming has a more competitive edge when it comes to recruiting and retention as programs are seen as a perk with real value to individuals.

## Communicating The Program

At the heart of every program is communication. All announcements, notices, emails, reports, speeches, and publications reflect the wellness program whenever updates and information are delivered. It is a blend of marketing and information involving three aspects:

- Conveying the broader message, values, and purpose of the wellness program
- Disseminating details of interventions and wellness program updates
- Building brand awareness and acceptance of the wellness program

Depending on the size of your organization, the communications role may be done by one or more team members. First, decide who will be responsible for disseminating ALL communications to employees (and families if they are to be included). Then factor in the type of communications, frequency, and format etc. that you want to use. Additionally, determine **what** information the stakeholders require and **how** and **when** they want to receive it.

Facilitating effective communication is multi-faceted and everyone's time is valuable therefore a Communications Management Plan will need to be created and its details shared with the team members and executive management.

The first level of communication is the announcement of support for starting a wellness program by the executive sponsor and thereafter, the frequency of communication and the best fit for the company culture can be molded around different formats to keep announcements fresh and interesting.

Consider the following aspects:

- Vary the method of communication and communicate, communicate, communicate!
- Communication materials should be personalized to the wellness program brand and integrate the information gathered from HR regarding demographics, language, and age and gender of the employees that the communication is directed towards.
- Ensure there are NO surprises. Stakeholders must be kept up-to-date on the progression of the wellness program, and this means providing the positive and any negative feedback.

- Promotion requires clear marketing and communication of the message as well as events.
- Establish guidelines on the sharing of information, testimonials, success stories, placing posters in high-traffic areas, posting of e-information, and Q&A.
- Use the intranet for website, newsletters, information pages on wellness, benefits, and employee success stories.
- Follow appropriate in-house policies and guidelines for incorporating the use of social media, twitter, corporate newsletter, and the intranet.
- Be knowledgeable about data security.
- Carefully file all information and correspondence.
- Establish networking groups for employees who are participating in a program and don't see each other regularly such as shift-workers or off-site employees.
- Determine the preferred method of communication, such as email, dashboards, or excel spreadsheets. Know what and how the information will be communicated and to whom.

Make announcements to employees advising them that a wellness program is being launched and seek out areas to involve them during the developmental stages. Speculation will most likely take place regarding what a wellness program means, what the impact is, who is involved and why. It is important to fend off conjecture and set the program on a good foundation so that the anticipation about the impending launch is positive. Regular updates will inform employees about what will be happening, provide opportunities to demonstrate appreciation for their assistance, and confirm the anticipated launch date.

Communication has multiple facets and ameliorates engagement barriers by providing awareness, teaching managers about the importance of empowering employees to participate, and helping to initiate personal changes. Variety is important too. Seasonal events, for example, will affect the program design due to holidays, vacations, or whether it is summer or winter. A program consistently needs fresh publicity and reminders and this must be factored in when planning an event and deciding whether it will have multiple sessions or be a stand-alone event.

## Vary The Channels

Use a variety of channels to promote the message, deliver updates, and provide supportive messages. If families are included in the program, then the information needs to be conveyed in a suitable delivery system to reach them too.

Examples of communications channels include updates at all-hands quarterly conferences that can be face-to-face as well as concurrently via a video/audio call for non-office based workers, email announcements and reminders, monthly emailed newsletters, use of IT to deliver a tip-of-the-day and daily supportive messages during health month, and video and podcast recordings of success stories.

Utilize your executive sponsor! Announcements about upcoming events and achievements take on added importance when communicated to employees by the executive sponsor of the program.

## Vary The Topics

Provide information about announcements, updates, changes to benefits, speakers, financial health, local community information, invitations to participate in sponsored walks and fun runs, and available resources.

The information provided does not always have to be created in-house. Tap into material that is available locally, from healthcare providers, or even from fitness apparel manufacturers for example. Be creative and think of the different avenues that you can utilize. Many fitness corporations are employing wellness specialists to talk to corporate organizations regarding their products and how they can be used to assist an individual's health plan. This can be useful for a lunch and learn session or included as a booth during the annual wellness fair. Negotiations can also be made to obtain group discounts.

You can see that the wellness team responsibilities cover multiple aspects of wellness from events, dissemination of information, managing budgets, coaching, and negotiation with vendors. Now we will take a closer look at defining the plan and creating a brand.

## Review Checklist

1. Determine the types of surveys to use
2. Identify the needs of employees
3. Identify the organizational needs
4. Incorporate the activities that employees are currently doing
5. Define a shared vision
6. Create S.M.A.R.T. goals
7. Establish the Communication Management Plan

8. Review the policies to determine what additional guidelines need to put in place
9. Develop a data security strategy

# CHAPTER 3

## Step Three: The Wellness Plan

*Defining The Plan And Developing A Wellness Brand.*

You can probably think of many projects that are announced or events that are advertised within your company but not many, if any, have a logo and a brand associated directly with them, other than the corporate logo. National companies spend millions of dollars to ensure that their brand is recognizable amongst consumers, and that users have a positive emotional response and will buy into the message and the product. In our everyday lives we are inundated with brands that we frequently recognize without even seeing a description of the product. In the same way, your wellness brand will represent the message and values of the program and be used in all communications, emails, IT, social media, and even marketing products like T-shirts and coffee mugs. This type of engagement marketing helps grow the relationship and connectivity with employees in today's socially connected world and builds loyalty and value into the programs.

Creating a brand for the wellness program is a step that is often overlooked, however by designing a brand for the wellness program you create a product that will establish it as a permanent fixture rather than a series of events, is instantly recognizable, and allows employees to see it as belonging to the company. When you add in meaningful content, employees will recognize it by the name, colors, tag line, and logo regardless of the medium used.

The earlier research into the culture of the organization combined with the mission statement for the program will show what is important or relevant and highlight potential areas where employees can connect with the company's philosophy and the shared wellness vision.

## The Wellness Plan

The project plan has various moving parts and has to monitor progress in relation to the objectives, financial obligations, the people who will be involved, the skills they will use on the wellness program, and demonstrate that the wellness program is on track to meet the approved goals. It will also have to ascertain how to integrate benefits, policies, workers compensation etc. into the wellness program. Additionally, the project plan creates a path that the team members can follow. If you do not have formal project management training you should be aware of the nine knowledge areas related to running a project and managing the scope and the inevitable request for changes that will occur as the wellness program develops and breathes life.

The project management handbook (PMBOK) refers to the following areas of management:

- Integration
- Scope
- Time
- Cost
- Quality
- HR
- Communication
- Risk
- Procurement

Once tasks are assigned, they will need to be prioritized. What is the expected start date to roll out the wellness program? Put a time-line in place using an excel spreadsheet to determine both the order of importance and the dates by which they need to be completed to ensure that you oversee the completion of the tasks and manage the different aspects of the program. Multiple items can have the same priority number if subsequent items depend on them for their progress. As you have seen, research and data is therefore one of the first major items that needs to be obtained. Keeping the shared vision and mission statement in front of the team helps with establishing purpose and meaning to the intention behind the plan and the objectives associated with the actions.

## The Healthy Organization

Employee health is linked to organizational health however technological advancements, physical environment, and work demographics are struggling to keep up with the demands of an ever-evolving world. Worker health has a profound effect not only at an organizational level, but also at a state and countrywide level too. A company's topmost strength is its employees and in order to be more flexible and proactive, the company's approach to wellness must focus on more than the individual's physical or nutritional health and basic interventions such as smoking cessation or weight control. While these programs are part of the overall wellness strategy, other components that draw on improving work-life balance and resilience such as skills growth and training should be included. In addition to health programs, the workspace environment and any job-sharing or shift-work should be explored as a means of offering a work setting that is conducive to all aspects of an individual's and a group's morale, growth, and health.

Furthermore, gaps in skills can be analyzed using qualitative tools to better understand what other talents are required. This includes hiring people who are passionate about what they do, utilizing existing employees who excel, and highlighting wellness champions who will be role-models and elevate the enthusiasm and engagement. This goes a long way in creating a healthy working environment that reduces stress and promotes personal growth while improving the organization's strength as a company where people are excited to work there.

## Branding The Program

The wellness program is directed towards everyone in the company and building a well-defined brand that the entire organization can identify with in order to heighten connectivity and loyalty to the program. Treat your program like any product; if it is not branded or promoted, no one will know about it and no one will buy it. Perhaps the company colors are perfect to incorporate into the logo, or perhaps there is a popular product that can be woven into the title. Develop a name for the overall program that is recognizable and relatable and tie it in with a tag line that resonates with the culture of the company. It can be a serious slogan or tongue in cheek, such as Well For Life! or Be Healthy! or For the Health of It! or even Fit Happens!

Basically anything that is connected to the program, either as information, emails, educational material, associated merchandise, posters, mugs, T-shirts, and even balloons or an incentive give-away will have the brand logo, slogan and or colors printed or attached to it. A branded program creates recognition, raises participation during events, assists communication, and elevates engagement.

This is an ideal task to assign to the marketing department however if your company is smaller then the wellness team will need to brainstorm ideas. Consider creating a naming competition for the wellness program and give a reward for the winning name and or tag line. This adds an element of fun and sets the tone that while the company is dedicated to making a lasting program, it can be enjoyable to participate in. Prior to the program launch, celebrate with a big reveal and a naming ceremony to kick-start the connection to the brand.

## Building A Wellness Community

Outstanding programs are ones that are tailored to meet not only health needs, but provide better communications and social interfaces with the employees. This promotes unique conditions for a wellness community to grow and evolve as the dynamics of the organization change in response to the enforcement of new policies that make it possible to have not only a healthier workplace but provides knowledge that can be applied at home too. Placing an emphasis on the importance of health, fitness, and well-being in all its forms, helping people to move from the "I'm thinking about it" to "I want to do it" mind-set, and making it easy to make small changes encourages people to participate in healthy activities and fosters a shared collective of mutually supportive groups and personal successes.

Multiple factors weave themselves together to create the healthy environment in the workplace and they are similar to many of the features found in a small town. There will be social and support groups, education portals, assistance programs, social media platforms, interaction with personnel, and access to an intranet. The subtleties of nurturing and growing the program involve a hands-on approach to know what employees expect and need as the program progresses and provide updates on the continuing benefits and positive impact of the program. Your own intranet can be used in new ways:

- Create a collaborative connection to co-workers
- Allow employees to share their own testimonials to motivate and encourage others who may not have participated yet
- Ask questions from the employees to the wellness team
- Get feedback about existing or proposed programs
- Find information on incentives or benefits
- Review upcoming events

This is particularly relevant for off-site and shift workers, as scheduled events need to be accessible for these employees too. Encouraging employees to contribute to the communications mediums that disseminate information further enhances camaraderie. Newsletters, a write-up in an email, and recognition on the wall of success boost connectivity and a community experience while keeping the program visible. This new wellness community can also encourage the development of goal-setting as either a private or group activity and produce actions that cultivate awareness and ongoing support in achieving steps to attaining the particular goal.

## Promotion

Linked to communication is the promotion of events, successes, and information related to the ever-changing aspects of the wellness program. The wellness team will therefore need to focus on developing a program that is both fun and meets the mission of the executive leadership. The creative output and unique style will tie in the brand and logo in all the communications materials in order to make it relevant. People process information in ways that are personally relevant therefore announcements and interactions should be flexible, varied, and tailored to suit the employees, being aware of their access to computers, literacy, and even the main language spoken.

Promotion is made easier if the information is readily available and visible, so this involves noticing the areas where employees gather, which stairwells and entrances are used, and varying the methods to deliver the message based on the learning styles best suitable for the workforce. For example, posters promoting a walking program (with the brand colors and logo) can be placed in dining areas, stairwells, or elevators. A tip of the day can stream across the home page during a designated wellness month. The idea of a wellness month is covered in chapter six. Promotion is therefore about engendering a personal connection and increasing participation in events. Specific promotional ideas are discussed throughout the book, but ultimately it is an opportunity to be as creative and professional as you can.

## Building A Website

Branding and promotion go hand-in-hand with the development of a website devoted to the wellness program. Collaboration with the IT department is key for the brand and the ongoing projects and events associated with the program.

IT will utilize many of the wellness team's ideas and make them a reality e.g. take the brand and logo and work them into a website or the benefits information page within the company intranet. Employees will then be able to go to a specific area to locate all aspects of wellness information, incentives, benefits, financial information, a calendar of events, updates and success stories, and FAQ as well as have a platform to share their own goals and accomplishments. There are additional uses of the wellness site; for example during an annual "wellness month" positive messages or the tip-of-the-day can be sent via email or as a banner heading that can scroll at the top of the home page. Decisions should also be made around connecting IT and the wellness program with social media, Twitter etc. and who will act as moderator(s) on different sites to enable employees to contribute their success stories and questions and permit an even spread of contributors. This needs to be monitored by a designated IT representative so that the website can stay current with the ever-evolving technology platforms, apps and sites.

## The Psychology Of Change

If you talk to any business owner they will tell you at length how wonderful great referrals are. Think about the numerous on-line review sites that are available for restaurants and hotels and how useful they are especially if you are considering going to one that you haven't tried before. Other people's opinions matter and the more positive reviews that you read, the more likely you are to take the plunge and make a reservation. The subtle psychology that surrounds decision-making and trying something new is particularly relevant to wellness: shifting the mind-set from thinking about changing, to actually making small changes, setting realistic goals, and maintaining positive behavior.

Change is not that easy though. It involves multiple thought processes, feelings, and reactions around a willingness to transform the current way of being. Tie all of this into an upcoming wellness program and you can see how using multiple mediums including the proactive use of the wellness champions will greatly assist the delivery of information, the promotion of the wellness program, and ease the transition of change.

At different stages of the expansion of the wellness program, employees will vary in their levels of interest in interventions, the personal relevance, and the pros and cons of responding to particular behavior changes. Your wellness programming is therefore geared to creating a structure that promotes awareness of existing behaviors, supports new ideas, and demonstrates a social commitment to new behavior.

## Planning, Purpose, And Quality

The wellness program is a major undertaking and requires a solid workable plan built upon the experience, passion, and imagination of the team members as well as the acquired data. Thorough preparation is key to major projects such as laying the foundation to build a house or preparing to paint a wall.

Likewise, to prepare for developing the interventions, the wellness team should have completed all their preliminary designated tasks such as employee demographics, health and wellness needs surveys, and the data analyzed and used to bring the executives up-to date with the progress. Now this information will assist the formation of a highly detailed roadmap with the interventions, policies, guidelines, and actions that meet the wellness program mission meticulously itemized and described. This is the project plan that, once completed, will need approval by the executive management prior to execution, be referenced by team members and shareholders alike, and require written authorization to change. The detailed plan will be referenced frequently and translate the team's innovative ideas into exciting programs.

When the data has been accumulated and analyzed, it is then time to draw up the structure of the wellness program with defined roles of the wellness team, utilization of the different departments that they represent, financial implications, analysis and reporting, and the steps required to meet the wellness vision. Chapter four will examine the essential interventions and events in-depth however the justification and criteria for selecting specific interventions needs to be decided beforehand. The program design also needs to consider the financial element and how it applies not only to the costs to bring an intervention to the employees, but the potential for an economic barrier or burden that prevent some employees from participating in events.

Remember, the wellness program is a partnership consisting of the employer, the employees, the vendors, and even the community and there are multiple actions that the wellness team will undertake in order to influence

these relationships through the interventions and via the program as a whole. Developing and managing the planning process encompasses brainstorming innovative ways to become agents of change, detailing all of the resources required to conceive, produce, and deliver the programs, and devising multiple ideas that can be filed for future events.

A flexible approach that combines all of these aspects works best at making small and steady steps, preventing the fall-out if employees are not on-board with the program.

## Executive Updates

Throughout the program there will be multiple evaluations and updated reports that need to be communicated to the executive member of the wellness team, prior to the main presentation to the entire executive team. Another role of the program manager is to manage communication, including the dissemination of information with senior management and it is helpful to know beforehand what the preferred method of communication is and the manner in which leaders want to be informed.

The executive sponsor will also review the information as it becomes available. Executive leaders need to be informed regarding the plan outline and anticipated outcomes, as this provides them with another opportunity to evaluate the proposed plan and offer their insight and experience and make suggestions that they wish to be incorporated. Once this has occurred, an ongoing visible show of support from management will further validate the program as without this level of interaction, the program can become stalled due to miscommunication and misdirected expectations.

How the leaders in the company communicate and engage with the employees, such as effectively communicating a message to foster engagement through the use of motivational language, plays a significant role in sustaining commitment to the wellness program as well as other areas of the business.

**Small Steps**

Having a ceremony to acknowledge the official launch of the wellness program is a great way to share the brand, who is involved, who to contact, expectations, and some of the interventions that will roll out in the coming weeks and months. While this may be a significant occasion, you may wish to consider having the first intervention be a small event that is short in duration rather than a large rollout that lasts for months. Some ideas include arranging for an ergonomic specialist to do a presentation and demonstration on upright desk options, or inviting local organic vendors to take and deliver weekly orders for fresh produce, or a "Project Zero" competition around holiday time with the purpose of not gaining weight.

Keeping it small will make it manageable and provide important information on costs, engagement, education needs, and other resources required. This is effectively a trial run that will encompass all the structures that you have put into place for the program and can be run in parallel to other initiatives such as launching the wellness intranet and teaching employees to explore this new tool, phasing in alternative vending machine selections, or offering new menu choices.

When learning any new skill one does not start at the most difficult level. Small steps are taken where knowledge can be mastered and success guaranteed.

Likewise when introducing a program, it should be structured to provide fun and promote ongoing interest and sign-ups. If an intervention is too tough early on, participants become discouraged and future interventions struggle to succeed, whereas success leads to more success. The interventions may provide information as well as create an opportunity for behavior change where participants weigh up the advantages and disadvantages of the change, examine how they will be affected, and what it means to them personally.

Start the program off slowly and positively, promote methods that show approval for change, and make it easy and convenient to effect change. Consider using senior executives to participate in a showcase event that actively promotes behavior change and breaks down barriers to change. At this early stage of launching the wellness program it is imperative that positive benefits of participation outweigh the effect of continuing as normal in order to demonstrate that early successes are possible. Empowerment and engagement are explored at length in the next chapters as we take a closer look at creating and promoting cornerstone programs.

### Review Checklist

1. Define and create the wellness brand
2. Expand and update the program plan
3. Organize a naming contest for the wellness program
4. Start to build the wellness community
5. Ensure that the program design improves the ability to engage and motivate employees
6. Establish a calendar of interventions
7. Set a mini-launch date
8. Present details of the plan to the executive team

# CHAPTER 4

## Step Four: CULTURE

*Supporting Sustainable Change Through*
*Empowerment And Engagement.*

The shared wellness vision and acquired data are at the forefront of defining the direction of the overall program, however before selecting the types of interventions you will implement, the wellness approach should also be crafted within the parameters of the existing culture while being mindful that the corporate culture will undergo periods of transition.

In order to meet the long-term wellness goals, the structure of your program needs to be open and inclusive, affordable, fit in with work schedules, and include tools to help with creating new habits at home and in social environments too. This means providing opportunities that will both educate and build lasting change through the delivery of a flexible, *holistic* approach to wellness while supporting an employee's participation to replace long-held behaviors with new healthier ones, no matter where they are on their wellness journey.

The early data that you gathered related to existing healthy activities that employees do in their life outside of the office will greatly assist in structuring the types of initiatives and policies that can further support engagement and enthusiasm for programs. For example, if employees are focusing on losing weight, then healthy choices in the vending machine or a lunch and learn series with a dietician can further reinforce what they are doing at home. Someone who participates in marathons may welcome flexi-time in order to fit in the longer runs that are necessary prior to a race, and if a local charity is involved it can be supported through corporate fundraising.

You may want to consider adopting an inclusive response to the information that you have gathered by incorporating programs that are non-illness, disease, or behavior related such as offering classes in new trends in fitness or providing yoga or meditation classes during lunch. This can also include fun lifestyle programs like weekly chair massages and/or manicures.

You can see that there are multiple ways to propagate a culture of wellness, a culture that is fun and encouraging rather than an environment that is perceived as mainly for employees who are unhealthy or at-risk and therefore nothing to do with the majority of employees. The tendency is to gravitate towards a program that is constructive, positive, and productive as typically, people want to be involved in something that has purpose, is meaningful to them, and that they feel they have a connection with.

Furthermore, no one wants to feel targeted or perceived among their peers as "needing" to attend "that weight-loss" program or unable to participate in a program that requires an individual to be able to run a race. There also needs to be consideration with regard to the personal cost to employees as interventions must be affordable from the type of clothing or equipment that is required by a participant, to any fees that may be involved.

The wellness environment reflects the habits, values, and principles that exist in the workplace and awareness of the culture should be used to initiate policies that will support the program, e.g. flexi-time, a tobacco-free organization, as well as examine what needs to be incorporated into the physical working space, what actions can be started to make healthy food options a reality, and continue to support a safe workplace. This is where asking the right questions in the early planning stages is strategically important to ensure that the overall program not only meets the company and employee needs, but offers a variety of interventions that tie in the purpose and value of the program and is suitable for a wider audience.

A holistic approach includes any connection to or volunteering in the local community, an emphasis on work-life balance, and supporting healthy endeavors at work and home. In doing so it demonstrates that the company is putting their people first, appreciating and respecting the lives of their employees, and ultimately creating a great place to work. When people feel their best, feel valued, and have a supportive environment and skills to make lasting change, their engagement and productivity increases.

## Influencing Learning

"Knowledge is power" and the methods you use to educate and deliver information will make a difference in how willing people will be to incorporate the material into their lives. Research has shown that people learn in a variety of different ways, often preferring one method to another. These include written communications, auditory messages via podcasts, telephone coaching, visual demonstrations and face-to-face interactions, and active participation in events rather than sitting in a classroom environment. Some people like to be directed to information (even told what to do) while others like to find out independently through reading and other forms of research. A variety of approaches can be utilized when advertising events, providing information, delivering interventions, and following up after the completion of programs. This needs to be factored in to ensure the best dissemination of information in order to reach the maximum number or target group of employees.

## Designing The Programs

When thinking about the components of programs and their timing there are three specific factors to consider:

**Positioning**: addresses the guidelines that will be in place to refine the visibility of each activity, the types of incentives that will be used, and how to use resources.

**Access**: aligns the needs of the employees with a variety of routes to access the programs, information, and opportunities for employees to provide feedback.

**Design**: considers the features that will be of interest to the targeted groups of employees. It examines in detail the activities and the promotion that is necessary to cultivate participation.

Together, these three areas integrate all the acquired data to facilitate interventions that are well-rounded, inclusive and offer variety in the categories, skills, and duration. No single program is likely to interest everyone, however by offering a menu of options based on the earlier needs-based survey you can provide choices that appeal to:

- The healthiest people in your organization
- Those who have been thinking about getting involved
- Those who are at-risk

This is a population-based approach and by not focusing on illness, you direct the general attitude to one of wellness and reinforce an air of positivity. Combined, these evoke the power of passion in creating a wellness program that gets results.

## Goal-Setting

This applies to participants working at setting personal goals, as well as the wellness team developing goals for each of the programs. In addition to the positioning, access, and design of programs the next area to consider are the tools that you will utilize. Some of these you will have already used, such as HRA's and employee surveys, and will employ again from time-to-time when required. Chapter five has a large section of incentives, including financial, intrinsic and extrinsic methods, physical resources, and coaching ideas that can motivate and engage when used appropriately.

The principles for the wellness programs are the same as those developed by an individual person and in this section we are going to explore goal-setting in detail. As outlined in chapter two, goals should be:

- **S**pecific - What specific goals need to be achieved.
- **M**easurable - quantify how to identify when success is attained.
- **A**ssignable (or actionable) - Who will do it and/or what actions will be done to achieve the goals.
- **R**ealistic - achievable goals based on available resources.
- **T**ime-related – specify when each result will be achieved.

In addition to the S.M.A.R.T. mnemonics you may want to consider integrating the W's; namely Who, What, When, Where, and Why in order to define the Goals, Objectives, and Resources that best fit your wellness plan. This means, for example, that when you are looking at developing a weight loss program you will want to know the following:

- Who specifically will the program be targeted towards? Who will be the project manager? Who will the supporting team members be?
- What is the desired outcome? What is the expected outcome?
- When and where will the program occur?
- Why is the outcome or purpose important?

The S.M.A.R.T. mnemonic combined with the W's helps with formulating a specific goal, clear and detailed objectives, and a well-defined review process. Clear goals will assist you in your planning, preparation, and policy-making. Objectives on the other hand, while similar to goals, have a distinct difference in that they define the *direction* that you wish to go. They are the detailed measurable steps that you need to take in order to attain your goal and should spur enthusiasm and drive within the wellness team as each objective is reached on the path to reaching the desired goal. Having a specific goal is important, as a general goal is too broad, and an intervention has to be relevant to the group targeted. The procedure of defining goals and objectives applies to the interventions, the policies, the evaluations, in fact all aspects of wellness programming.

| S.M.A.R.T. GOAL With W's | OBJECTIVE With W's | INTERVENTION With W's |
|---|---|---|
| To be a tobacco free workplace. | Reduce the number of smokers by 20 percent within 12 months. | Offer smoking cessation aids to participants such as patches, education, and support classes. Group coaching. Develop and implement tobacco policies. |
| Promote a healthy environment and support employees. Reduce the number of employees who are overweight to 30 percent within 18 months. | Reduce total weight by 15 percent within 18 months. Identify areas to replace foods with healthier choices. | Weight management programs, support groups. Initiate daily lunchtime walking groups. Appraise vending food and beverage machine selections. |
| Create a happy | Reduce the | Show prompt |

| and supportive work environment. | number of stressed employees by 20 percent within 6 months. Identify short and long term stressors. | appreciation to employees. Offer weekly onsite yoga/meditation classes. Provide financial counseling. Sleep management course. Time-management course. Have a weekly comedy DVD during Friday lunchtime. Survey to determine short and long term stressors. Introduce flexi-time. Develop and implement policies to support flexi-time. |
|---|---|---|

For example, staying with the concept of a weight loss program, the wellness team will have gathered the data and discovered that 45 percent of the employees are significantly overweight. The team then chooses a S.M.A.R.T. goal to reduce the number of employees who are overweight to 30 percent within 18 months. This is a measurable goal with a start and end date, a specific number of employees to target, and a specific health risk to target.

The objectives are also measurable and set you on a clear path to attain the goals. The objectives of the S.M.A.R.T. goal to reduce the number of employees who significantly overweight by 15 percent within 18 months are the details of each of the goals and can be expressed such as the following:

- The weight loss intervention will start on January 1st and end on June 30th the following year for a total of 18 months
- 30-minute group and individual weekly coaching sessions will be permitted during company time (specific to the program e.g. nutrition or weight-loss coaching)
- Policies will be put in place by January 1st to enable new coaching regulations

You can see that objectives are the specific details that steer the direction of the program by focusing the team energy on the data, details, and desired outcome.

The progress and results of the particular intervention that is specific to the goal will need to be measured and requires agreed criteria for gathering and assessing the levels of attaining the anticipated outcome. A well-planned approach that incorporates specific goals and objectives will ensure that the intervention offers challenges that can be overcome, the participants can feel that they are making progress, and the wellness team can see if the program is on target.

Interventions need to be attainable and offer challenges to:

- Help individuals make real and ongoing progress
- Help them be accountable for their ongoing participation
- Recognize and reward the achievement of their individual goals

Interspersing regularly scheduled programs with a variety of other events maintains consistency while injecting fun and surprise to keep the overall wellness program feel fresh. Subsequent programs can be stand-alone or a step-by-step approach and this is particularly relevant in helping individuals see that they have attained a particular goal within a set timeframe and that they are making progress. Participants can then formulate new goals within a new timeframe and so the cycle of improvement continues.

**The Cornerstone Programs**

A wellness program is defined as one that has a "reasonable chance of improving the health of or preventing disease in participating individuals." Loeppke R. The value of health and the power of prevention. *Int J Workplace Health Management* 2008; I:95-108.

The cornerstone programs are the foundation of the wellness program because they will be in place for numerous years, are flexible so that they can respond to changes in demographics and technology, and can be customized to incorporate new research and evidence-based information. Four programs that are popular, based on needs are:

1. Stress reduction
2. Nutritional
3. Physical
4. Tobacco cessation

During the planning sessions for all programs, some of the areas to consider include:
- Who the interventions are aimed at?
- What policies and components will be put in place and used to achieve the expected outcome and benefits?

- When is the best time of day and year to implement a program?
- Where will it take place?
- Why has a specific program been chosen?
- How will it be launched to build daily engagement and make long-term behavior change possible?

Physical and nutritional programs are adaptable for both healthy and at-risk employees. The results of all programs can yield not only expected health benefits, but also the additional benefits of improved quality of life, an improved and healthier organization, and a healthier community.

## Stress Management

Stress affects everyone and impacts the workplace and the community. If permitted to go unchecked, stress builds up, revealing itself in the form of chronic illnesses that further drives up the costs of healthcare. In 2015, workplace stress was estimated to cost between 200 and 300 billion dollars annually, however some of the stressors are addressable through a variety of approaches and policies that companies can introduce and employees can take onboard. In fact, job stress is the main source of stress for American adults and with the result that it is more strongly associated with health complaints than financial or family problems.

A 2013 survey by the APA Center for Organizational Excellence also found that "more than one-third of working Americans reported experiencing chronic work stress and just 36 percent said their organizations provide sufficient resources to help them manage that stress." This presents you with a great opportunity to address what is, in fact, a growing problem and reverse the trend. There are numerous factors such as long hours, pressure from supervisors, unfulfilling projects, job insecurity, not being recognized for a job well done, and being excluded from decision-making that can trigger negative stress. When this type of stress is ongoing, with no relief, it becomes chronic, creating a cascade of symptoms including anxiety, a compromised immune system, and sleep disorders, that affect an individual at work and at home. Overcompensating for any of the symptoms, or trying to mask them, can manifest as the overconsumption of alcohol, overeating, unhealthy living, and even misusing drugs.

Stress management is an ever-growing area and can often be woven through all other programs and have physical elements as well as educational components. Topics include the following: financial wellness, sleep management, elder care and child-care, physical programs, nutritional counseling, yoga, and meditation. Be aware of the areas within your own organization that may contribute to chronic stress, rather than *eustress*, which is temporary, motivational, and associated with increased energy and a zest for life. Consider cultural changes that can be made to support employees while providing them with information on recognizing stress within themselves and learning how to relax.

## Policies

Deciding the types of interventions that will be offered based on the needs assessments and other information acquired to enable good decision-making may also require a change in some policies or the creation of new policies. When considering any offering, check if the intervention complies with policies that are already in place. Depending on the hierarchy structure of your organization, a new policy can take several weeks to implement as approvals are sought and the HR and legal department signs off on it. The policies are written guidelines to enable employees and managers to take part in the various programs either at their place of work or an off-site location. Policies should also be written to comply with ALL legal requirements.

Generally, policies will cover:

- Paid work-time to participate in health promotion activities
- Expanding sick-leave to include caring for/looking after a sick child or adult family member
- Annual Health Risk Assessments
- Aspects of health and safety
- Education and training
- Compliance with government regulations
- Space for lactating mothers

Additionally, policies will also cover what is NOT permitted e.g. smoking on premises (unless a designated area is allocated).

Remember, these are only some of the areas that policies related to wellness programming will cover. The aim when starting a wellness program or reinvigorating an existing program is to focus on the known factors and identify which risks are modifiable through interventions such as increased physical activity, education, better nutrition, tobacco cessation, workplace yoga, financial wellness, and stress reduction techniques to minimize the probability of chronic disorders occurring or worsening.

## Nutritional Policies

A report by Finkelstein et al., 2009 estimated that the health care costs related to obesity in 2008 were a staggering $147 billion! Good food choices are a foundation of most health programs in helping an individual stay fit, able to do their job, and reduce risk factors such as high blood pressure, obesity, or diabetes. Behavior change should therefore be linked to not only an individual's diet and nutrition but also to a wider setting via changes in workplace policies to foster personal changes.

You may decide that the main thrust of a nutritional program at its commencement should be on weight-loss, so it is important that policies are in place, for example, to enable appropriate choices to be made. Areas that are impacted, in this instance, include vending machines, types of food available in the cafeteria, at meetings, holiday parties, special occasions like birthdays, and making healthy food the cheaper option. Think about your own work environment and look at the spaces and situations where food or snacks are available. Policies can help you provide an environment where healthy eating is made possible during the typical workday, is not more costly, and fits in with the mission of the intervention by promoting health and minimizing health risks through a nourishing and wholesome food regime.

The United States government provides dietary guidelines regarding the recommended fluids, proteins, carbohydrates, fats, and vitamins and minerals that men and women should typically consume and is a good resource when planning changes to the types of food offered in the workplace and when providing educational sessions. Ideas to adopt include replacing trans/hydrogenated/saturated fats with non-saturated oils when cooking food, having healthier food and nutrition options as defined by the latest government standards in vending machines, a reduction in the availability of sugary drinks, and sourcing locally grown organic foods.

It is not the place of the wellness team to monitor what employees are consuming, but to enable choices to be made by the employees that support their ongoing healthy behavior not only at work, but by creating a health habit that overflows into every-day living and builds into healthy choices in many areas of life. Obtain input from employees regarding nutritional requests that they wish to have. The wellness team can assist in making certain options available in subtle ways, such as having the cafeteria menu offer sweet potato fries as well as regular potato fries, make potato fries more expensive than sweet potato fries, reduce the price of vegetables and salads, and offer more vegan and vegetarian choices. All changes should be eased in gradually so that employees become used to new foods and be willing to try a new item, rather than having to take it (or leave it) because their usual food is no longer on the menu. Additional policies can also be made to support the sourcing, purchasing, storage, and preparation of the healthier food options.

These changes will start to positively influence alter the environment of the organization into one that proactively supports all aspects of health beyond the cafeteria and expands into meeting rooms with better i.e. healthier, choices of beverages, cookies, fruits during meetings. In return the workplace becomes an actively healthier environment.

**Examples of Nutritional Policies**

- Healthy snack and drink options listed in vending machines
- At least 75 percent of vending food and drink to meet nutrition guidelines
- Minimum 30 percent of healthy food and drink to be provided on-site
- Revised pricing in cafeteria with subsidies for healthier alternatives
- Meetings to be catered with healthy food
- Establish worksite healthy food and beverage purchase guidelines
- Serve fresh and minimally processed foods
- Offer a variety of foods that are low sodium, gluten free, vegan and meet the dietary requirements of diabetics and other people with special dietary requirements
- A designated dining area, to lessen incidences of employees eating at their desk
- Strict policy on use of the employee refrigerator to ensure that employees comply with food safety guidelines e.g. removal of all food on Friday afternoon at a designated time, non-stacking of food containers
- Sanitation guidelines for employee refrigerator, freezer, and kitchen equipment
- Posting nutritional information in dining and cafeteria areas

Using the S.M.A.R.T. tool, select a few of the programs that you wish to implement, have the policies in place, and work with the various departments such as catering and marketing to ensure that the campaigns are manageable and the changes will not overwhelm everyone. Starting with simple modifications to menus and clearly posted nutritional information will allow food choices to be easier and help individuals make a healthier transition.

Communicate with the catering department to source local food choices and build affiliations with vendors in order to generate new ideas related to food options and nutrition. The changes to the menu should be subtle and gradual so a timescale needs to be drawn up to ensure that an end date is decided for when the transitions will be fully integrated.

Campaigns related to new foods, food tastings, and nutritional values will educate employees about the importance of, and how to make, better food choices ranging from menu planning, shopping, to actual cooking. Material can come from the government *Food Guide Pyramid*, local state guidelines, and dieticians and nutritionists who can give a presentation during lunch breaks.

It can also be fun to include the catering manager or a chef to offer a tour of the kitchen or do blind food tastings, as competitions are a way to create awareness around different food as something to try and not be wary of.

Remember to include input from the employees too, as there may be one food that the majority will simply NOT do without and you don't want to start a protest!

## Additional Ideas

- Provide employees with access to a weekly delivery of local produce from a farmers market or a local organic bakery

- Have recipes available that use some of the fruits and vegetables sold at the market, especially the unusual produce
- Hold a bi-annual nutrition experience month e.g. during a Spring and Fall month to explore the flavors of these seasons
- Create a library of online resources, recipes, and cookbooks
- Hold nutritional education classes on creating menus to support healthy eating and weight loss. Tap into health educators at local universities, colleges, and hospitals. These institutions are also a great resource of online information that employees can utilize if they have dietary questions
- Develop menus with calorie counts, nutritional information, high fiber, low calorie, heart healthy etc.
- Hold lunch and learn demonstrations from dieticians, chefs, local restaurants, and samples of food from farmers markets and organic suppliers. Additional topics can include coping with stress, foods for vitality and energy, as well as the obvious weight reduction foods
- Invite a chef to demonstrate a cooking lesson, perhaps using an unusual vegetable or spice. It's fun, interactive, and the recipe is take home too
- Hold a catered breakfast or lunch to coincide with health month
- Plant a garden or volunteer at a community garden

## Physical Policies

A 2009 meta-analysis study in the Journal of Preventive Medicine examined findings from 1969 to 2007 comprising 38,231 subjects. The authors concluded that while most adults do not achieve adequate physical activity levels, physical activity interventions in the workplace actually improved health and contributed to a positive outcome.

Combining physical activity with nutritional guidelines and policies further enhances their positive effects; therefore all policies should be constructed with co-relationships in mind. There are numerous studies that demonstrate the causal link between exercise and nutrition, and evidence of these can be seen in successful training and weight-loss programs. Additionally, America's Health Rankings posts the top 10 healthiest states and the 10 least healthy states, demonstrating the link between environment and urban planning policies. For example, walkable communities with recreational facilities and access to healthy foods are more active and less obese than other towns and this information should be useful when you are considering the types of policies that you plan to put in place.

## Examples Of Physical Policies

- Provide on-site space and access to exercise, yoga, and meditation classes
- Offer annual discount for participation at an off-site fitness club
- Permit flexi-time to allow employees time off to participate in charity sporting events
- Develop a policy regarding the use of wearables, apps, and maintaining fitness logs

- Permit flexi-time to allow employees time off to participate in physical events, meditation, or stress reduction activities during the workday. Be specific regarding what is included and excluded
- Ensure stairways are accessible, well-lit, clean, and attractive to use.
- Permit up to 30-minute walking, stretching, and quiet-time breaks during the workday
- Ensure that breaks occur during meetings lasting over one hour

Studies show that when energy moves, people feel more alert, have more drive to be productive at work and in their private life, and are more resilient to withstand shifts and stress in their life. The results of the previous needs-preference studies will allow the wellness team to tailor the programs to meet employees halfway by offering opportunities to participate and live better, feel connected to their work, and engender accountability for ones actions. This is a move away from the early style of wellness programs that focused on the negative aspects of risk factors and statistics, towards a program that centers on positive messages of confidence, commitment, and wellness. The holistic approach seamlessly integrates both work and home life, no matter where along the wellness path the individual may be. For the company, inclusive activities build a strong sense of community, loyalty, and engagement that translates into healthy organizational performance.

**Additional Ideas**
- Subsidize membership at an off-site facility, or offer monthly or annual reimbursement for participation

- Provide wireless headsets to let people walk around while on calls.
- Consider ergonomic chairs, desks, workstations, and encouraging employees to stand at a desk rather than sit
- Provide cycle storage racks and designated bike parking area
- Provide lockers
- Organize behavior-change programs that will encourage daily use to effect long-term change
- Provide pedometers
- Create a library of local walking trails, bike paths, fitness books, and DVD's
- Organize a lunchtime walking group
- Encourage group movement away from desks for sedentary workers
- Provide the opportunity to practice a new activity such as organizing a stair-walking plan, rather than using elevators
- Invite local instructors to demonstrate their discipline during a designated health month e.g. yoga, meditation, massage, martial arts, stress reduction. Negotiate discounts for participation in their classes
- Establish walking routes during lunch breaks. Encourage group participation
- Consider talking to your health insurance of benefits provider to negotiate lower rates for employees who participate regularly in physical activities

## Tobacco Cessation Policies

There is substantial evidence that tobacco cessation policies work best when used in conjunction with other initiatives, be they government, state, or local guidelines. The World Health Organization recommends a supportive approach combined the commitment by the individual (with either behavioral and/or pharmacological interventions) to promote tobacco cessation.

Work place tobacco cessation policies have been found to reduce the consumption of tobacco products (cigarettes in particular), protect non-smokers from passive smoking, and are more likely to encourage smokers to quit. Funding for tobacco cessation programs are available in all 50 states and the District of Columbia, with the amount of the funding varying from state to state. Further, the American Lung Association states that tobacco is the leading cause of preventable death in the USA.

Workplace tobacco cessation policies have the benefit of being inadvertently supported by national campaigns in the media, combined with tax increases on tobacco, which further leads to a reduction in the usage of tobacco products. While New Year's Day is the most common time for people to try to stop smoking, only an average 8 percent will succeed in achieving their resolution. In order to augment motivation and participation, consider implementing tobacco policies in conjunction with the resolutions and subsequent "National Stop Smoking Campaigns" when your in-house promotional efforts will be enhanced with national and regional advertising in the media. Your promotional efforts and educational and support programs should occur during the tobacco cessation program and also afterwards, in order to prevent relapse.

## Examples of Tobacco Cessation Policies

- A no smoking policy will begin on a specific date
- Advertising of tobacco products is prohibited
- Smoking is not permitted in company offices, premises, or company vehicles
- Smoking is permitted in a designated area either inside or outside of the building
- Smoking is not permitted at the front of the building or the side that is visible to clients
- Smoking is permitted during working hours. Your organization may choose to specify the frequency of the activity if this is permissible in your state
- The sale of all tobacco products, including chewing tobacco, is prohibited on company premises
- Free or low-cost smoking cessation programs will be available at all workplace locations

## Additional Ideas

- Offer free or subsidized coaching sessions
- Offer educational material from health care providers
- Offer free smoking cessation aids
- Offer meditation classes
- Monitor the potential concentration of smoke building up in the designated smoking area

Secondhand smoke contains over 50 known carcinogens and is therefore dangerous for both the smoker and nonsmoker. While there are Federal health regulations that should be adhered to, there may also be state and town regulations that should also be incorporated into your programming. Consider providing training for managers on enforcing policies and educating their team on the hazards of second-hand smoke

**Wearables**

While these devices are useful tools to have alongside existing programs, they are not programs nor are they tools that are ideal for everyone. They can help people monitor their daily fitness efforts, their cardio health, provide reminders to move and be active, and stay-connected to a wellness program. When combined with mobile apps, they can influence better health choices and decisions.

This technology is useful in a business setting by helping to encourage employees to monitor their health and actions and make better choices. However, it will need to be monitored from a "use at work" perspective, with policies to support their utilization. Currently, common wearables are pedometers, cardio trackers, and health-watches and they are a useful addition to monitoring personal accountability at work and at home. However new tools are appearing annually so the wellness team needs to stay current with devices, apps, and other technology as today's devices can very quickly become obsolete.

Additionally, from a security and compliance perspective, many of these items are small with the ability to not only track personal data but also have the potential to transmit confidential company information. This means that your organization needs to be up-to-date with the available technology, create guidelines and policies to aid their use and application in the workplace, and how to address any misuse and violations.

Wearables have their place as a tool to support ongoing participation in programs and as a motivation aid.

## Conveying The Wellness Message

Creating a brand is not only a marketing aid, it is a means of aiding the promotion and awareness of all interventions while helping employees to feel connected to the wellness program as a whole. Once you have decided which program you want to begin with, you can formulate your marketing plan and build a campaign around it. No matter the size of your organization, if you want to rally people to participate then you need to be organized and clear on what you want to share and how you want to disseminate the information. Without a plan, there can be confusion around the programming in general, uncertainty, lack of enthusiasm, and all the hard work and research will have been wasted. This is not a word-of-mouth campaign.

Here are a few general marketing prompts and ideas that you can adapt to use with not only your cornerstone programs, but future programs too. Be as creative as you can in conveying the ideas to make them fresh and fun and vary the types of media that you use:

- To encourage physical activity, display posters and signs at elevators, (point of decision prompts)
- Display posters near to parking areas to encourage employees to park further from the entrance
- Display nutritional information posters in cafeteria and near vending machines

- Have less healthy options in vending machines placed in higher or lower positions so that the healthier options are easily visible
- Have paper placemats that show nutritional information, portion sizes.
- Provide nutritional information at the decision-making source
- Use motivational before-after photographs from employees near dining areas, elevators, and in a designated area for a "wall of success"
- Provide opportunity for employee feedback. Ensure employees know how to do this
- Send emails with nutritional values of foods or meals available at the company
- Display Department of Health posters promoting the latest food pyramid and daily fruit and vegetable requirements
- Stay up-to-date with community events that employees can participate in
- Policy changes can be sent via email to update existing policies. New policies can be made available in a public display board, by weekly team meetings with managers, as well as via email updates

**Wellness Champions**

The cheerleaders of the program are the wellness champions and they will be fully involved now as you kick-off the first of the wellness interventions. They do not need to be a perfect or skilled participant with personal results that are unattainable by an individual who is going to sign up for a program. If you can, assign champions to an intervention that has meaning to them, allowing them to share their passion with colleagues before and during the program. A lot is expected of them as interventions can be a one-time stand-alone session or may run weekly, monthly, or for several years. Wellness champions will be expected to consistently offer ongoing enthusiastic support and positively influence their team, department, or peers by being engaged, available, and personable. Remember, the champion's role is one of campaigner and advocate, rather than one of winner.

**Wellness Coaches**

A wellness coach is a wonderful investment and addition to the team. Regardless of whether the coach is a full-time employee or a consultant, this trained professional can bring unique insight into the design of each intervention, assist with the development of a program, and work to keep participants motivated to complete their goals. Wellness coaches will listen to the expressed needs of employees, what employees feel that they can and cannot achieve based on perceived limitations, and help them to clarify their motivation to achieve.

As a program develops, the coach remains non-judgmental and on the side of the employee, helping them to see what is working, how to celebrate the successes (large and small), and can even offer referrals to other experts if a particular need is beyond their level of expertise such as financial counseling.

The coach is of particular help when a participant experiences a slow-down of results, fails to attend sessions, or thinks that they are not succeeding and cannot continue. The coach will explore what the employee has achieved, what they are able to do, and what options are still open to them. Any procrastination is lifted up and the bright light of their strengths shone on them to enable step-by-step progress to be made and goals to be achieved.

Coaches help employees who are taking part in a program to step back and think about their best vision of themselves in their best situation, to explore the gaps between where they are now and their best vision, and what strengths and talents they have that may have lain dormant for years that they can tap into and use again to move forward.

This is a two-way flow of energy as an abundance of positive reinforcement flows from the coach and an invigoration of drive and power emanates from the employee. It is at this moment that the employee believes in the strengths they can use, the strategies that they will put in place, and realizes that they are actually able to visualize and ultimately experience the rewards.

Coaching can be offered in groups, one-on-one, and more commonly via telephone or Skype in thirty-minute sessions weekly. Coaches will help program participants to realize that they can be successful, help them set clear goals, and establish a clear and definitive path to get to where they want to be.

**A Reminder About All Programs**
- As outlined in chapter one, programs should be offered to all employees.
- Health Risk Assessments (HRA's) can be offered to all employees to establish baselines for evaluations and programs to be built upon, to identify at-risk data, and determine what interventions should be started.
- After receiving HRA confidential results, some individuals may require a follow-up

appointment with their primary care physician to further interpret the results.

- Educational lunch and learn programs can offer general information on a broad range of topics such as tai-chi, DASH or Mediterranean diets, or the latest fitness apps or wearables.
- When holding a Wellness Fair, invite local health and wellness vendors, as they can offer a variety of disciplines and information that complement planned interventions.
- Healthcare providers and local hospitals can provide educational materials related to a specific condition and assistance with simple on-site health screenings such as cholesterol, blood pressure, and blood glucose levels that can be run annually.

Throughout all of the preparations for building the wellness program, you will have diligently conducted detailed research and planned each step with care and consideration in order to gauge the wellness, health, and well-being needs, establish the available funding, and determine the best interventions to initiate. Next, we'll take a look at strategies for managing your wellness program.

**Review Checklist**
1. Ensure the programming attracts healthy and at-risk employees
2. Create a program structure that is flexible to meet employees' needs and build lasting change
3. Include the three elements of Position, Access, and Design into the program

4. Formulate S.M.A.R.T. goals to define the Goals, Objectives, and Resources of interventions
5. Determine if new policies need to be initiated and if any existing policies need to be updated
6. Decide how will you disseminate new policies
7. Establish a marketing plan for the program

# PART II: Strategies For Managing Your Wellness Program

# CHAPTER 5

## Step Five: Generate Wins

*Recognize Contributions And Celebrate Victories*

As you acquire more information about the wellness needs of your organization, managing the various programs will require you to take on a more creative slant than before. By thinking about original intervention ideas, developing imaginative methods to engage employees, and fostering resourceful ways to reward employees for their participation you can build unique programs that inspire and place your wellness brand ahead of the average worksite program. As a change agent, this requires you to be consciously creative in order to reach beyond the various interventions that have been established to initiate positive behavior-change. One of the tools that is frequently used is incentives, and these require careful planning with regard to their eventual implementation. While the purpose of the wellness program is to create lasting positive behavior change, the use of incentives is another tool that can assist in modifying health behavior, creating the desired transformation by motivating and rewarding employees and ultimately encouraging them to participate, complete activities, and continue pursuing their goals. Used appropriately for your organization, incentives can create a sense of interest and motivate participation in activities while offering a reward for the behavior. Used incorrectly, they can have the opposite effect and be costly.

While there are state and federal guidelines and regulations around the use of incentives, there are also tactical uses that you may want to consider and factor in when designing an incentive plan. The cornerstone programs of stress management, nutritional and physical wellbeing, and tobacco cessation are frequently the foundation of a wellness program, based on national statistics, and the correct incentives, or rewards, will allow you to build an amazing program that excites and motivates employees to get moving and reach for their best self. The right incentives can also send an underlying message that the company is dedicated to making the wellness program a success and wants the employee to succeed at achieving their personal health goals. Incentives have multiple uses including; as a reward for enrolling in an event, participation in an intervention, completion of objectives, and annual membership of a gym or fitness class. They can encourage participation in interventions and when used carefully, are a motivating factor in staying on track and pursuing personal goals.

**An Incentive Plan**

During the planning stage of your wellness program, consideration should be given to the promotion of the individual interventions, the incentives, as well as the overall wellness program. The interventions and their corresponding incentives will be woven into the plan, to keep employees engaged through a steady reward delivery system. Incentives are multi-fold and with this in mind you should consider how you will tie the identified needs, policies, and interventions to the purpose, size and types of incentives that you will use.

By now you will be clear on what the main health risks are for your organization, and will be able to offer incentives that will assist the motivation of the employees in continuing to reach for their goals. Incentives are closely linked to the time-scale of the intervention, therefore when structuring an incentive plan it must be reasonable in both the expectations and effort that is required to complete the activity in order to receive the actual reward. It is important to ensure that your incentive design complies with the current regulations pertaining to incentives, such as the monetary amount that can be offered annually, and does not violate any of the anti-discrimination laws.  Also, the remuneration must be worthwhile and reflect the amount of effort that has gone into achieving a particular goal or completing a task. After all, the whole aim of incentives it to motivate, not DE-motivate. A kickoff event should be included in this plan as it is a fun way of introducing the initiative and creating positive energy around the program.

### Participatory And Health-Contingent Programs

The Affordable Care Act has developed rules to support wellness programs and protect employees from unfair practices. Wellness programs fall into two categories: participatory and health-contingent. A participatory wellness program must be available to all, however it does not require an employee to meet any conditions related to their health. Examples of a participatory program are:

- Reimbursement for gym membership
- Free counseling or coaching
- Free training and educational classes
- Completion of an HRA without further action required

Health-contingent programs can offer rewards, however they require participants to meet a criterion related to their health such as lowering blood pressure, reducing cholesterol levels, or decreased tobacco use or smoking cessation. These programs also allow for employees to obtain rewards for other activities even if they are unable to attain a health target.

Additionally, health-contingent programs often use a "stick" rather than "carrot" incentive structure such as penalizing for tobacco use by imposing a higher premium and fall into two categories: activity-based programs and outcome-based programs.

Activity-based programs require the employee to complete a health activity, such as regularly participate in a lunchtime walking program for a fixed number of weeks, while outcome-based programs focus on the actual health of the employee and requires them to work towards stopping tobacco use or lowering cholesterol in order to attain a reward.

A U.S. Department of Labor (DOL) fact sheet on the Affordable Care Act and Wellness Programs, January 2014, provides the following guidelines regarding health-contingent programs to ensure protection for employees and offer flexibility for employers:

"In order to protect consumers from unfair practices, the proposed regulations would require health-contingent wellness programs to follow certain rules, including:

- Programs must be reasonably designed to promote health or prevent disease. To be considered reasonably designed to promote health or prevent disease, a program would have to offer a different, reasonable means of qualifying for the reward to any individual who does not meet the standard based on the measurement, test or screening. Programs must have a reasonable chance of improving health or preventing disease and not be overly burdensome for individuals.

- Programs must be reasonably designed to be available to all similarly situated individuals. Reasonable alternative means of qualifying for the reward would have to be offered to individuals whose medical conditions make it unreasonably difficult, or for whom it is medically inadvisable, to meet the specified health-related standard.

- Individuals must be given notice of the opportunity to qualify for the same reward through other means. These proposed rules provide new sample language intended to be simpler for individuals to understand and to increase the likelihood that those who qualify for a different means of obtaining a reward will contact the plan or issuer to request it.

- The proposed rules also implement changes in the Affordable Care Act that increase the maximum permissible reward under a health-contingent wellness program from 20 percent to 30 percent of the cost of health coverage, and that further increase the maximum reward to as much as 50 percent for programs designed to prevent or reduce tobacco use."

Health-contingent programs must also comply with HIPAA guidelines regarding non-discrimination and wellness programs. The U.S. DOL provides a fact sheet *FAQ's About The HIPAA Nondiscrimination Requirements.* It provides useful information on this and many other factors related to health-contingent programs in general, should you wish to implement these types of programs.

The following extract from this U.S. DOL fact sheet shows the five requirements for wellness programs which base a reward on satisfying a standard related to a health factor:

1. The total reward for all the plan's wellness programs that require satisfaction of a standard related to a health factor is limited – generally, it must not exceed 30 percent of the cost of employee-only coverage under the plan.
2. The program must be reasonably designed to promote health and prevent disease.
3. The program must give individuals eligible to participate the opportunity to qualify for the reward at least once per year.

113

4. The reward must be available to all similarly situated individuals. The program must allow a reasonable alternative standard (or waiver of initial standard) for obtaining the reward to any individual for whom it is unreasonably difficult due to a medical condition, or medically inadvisable, to satisfy the initial standard.
5. The plan must disclose in all materials describing the terms of the program the availability of a reasonable alternative standard (or the possibility of a waiver of the initial standard).

It is up to your organization to determine which type of incentive reward program is appropriate to use, in order to drive positive behavior and modify lifestyles, and whether your organization with adopt an employee-only model for its programs. Also consider what is the most appropriate fit for your organization's culture. Uncovering an individual's motivation for improved wellness, then coaching and supporting them through the various steps to transformation is therefore key to sustaining lasting change. It is also in line with recognizing an individual's contributions and celebrating their victories.

## Adding Incentives

What are the interventions that are most commonly incentivized? Health screenings and completion of the HRA currently hold the top spot and are incentivized over 75 percent of the time, followed by the cornerstone programs where rewards are offered to employees who participate in the various activities. According to a 2011 survey by The Horton Group, 90 percent of companies with an outcomes-based program also factor in monitoring blood-pressure, cholesterol, and smoking. Linking incentives to results is commonly used and your wellness plan will also determine if it is for employees only, or if retirees, part-timers, spouses and family members are also included. Regulations, as of January 1st 2014, require that all rewards should not exceed 30 percent of the total cost of benefits plan coverage. The proviso is that rewards should not exclude anyone based upon health or economic factors. While rewards must be inclusive, reasonable, and worthwhile they must also be achievable within a realistic timeframe. This means that the design of the interventions must also be practical and attainable in order to make the incentive possible, regardless of whether the aim is to participate or reach certain goals.

## Addressing The Main Health Concerns

The focus so far has been on offering incentives to employees, however from the employer's perspective the main health concerns that have been identified from HRA's and surveys also needs to be addressed. Financial rewards are a delicate balance, as you will need to ensure that the monetary amount is sufficiently high enough to merit action to participate, that the ability to succeed is realistically possible within a given time-frame by a large proportion of the employees, and that program targets do not penalize individuals who would be unlikely to achieve the desired target in the particular program. When factoring in the use, or not, of incentives, there are additional elements to consider based upon the early data gathered when creating a wellness plan, such as:

- Are the rewards of a sufficient size to motivate employees to participate?

- Do incentives fit in with the culture of the company?
- Will incentives be applicable to a large number of employees?
- Are the targets flexible enough to comply with company demographics?
- Is the incentive plan affordable based on the potential number of achievements

Flexibility in the design of the incentive program allows the wellness team to align it with the needs of employees and structure programs that will encourage progress, and ultimately success, in achieving long-term wellness goals rather than realizing a statistical accomplishment that cannot easily be built upon.

What should the size of the reward be in order to incentivize individuals? A 2009 study to determine the impact of incentives and their relationship to smoking cessation was conducted by Kevin G. Volpp, M.D., Ph.D., and his team and published in the New England Journal of Medicine. The study was held in a large multi-national company where 442 employees received information about smoking-cessation programs while 436 employees received information about the programs plus financial incentives. The financial incentives of the program were tiered. The following extract states that financial amounts were modest with:

"$100 for completion of a smoking-cessation program, $250 for cessation of smoking within 6 months after study enrollment, as confirmed by a biochemical test, and $400 for abstinence for an additional 6 months after the initial cessation, as confirmed by a biochemical test. Individual participants were stratified according to work site, heavy or non-heavy smoking, and income. The primary end point was smoking cessation 9 or 12 months after enrollment, depending on whether initial cessation was reported at 3 or 6 months. Secondary end points were smoking cessation within the first 6 months after enrollment and rates of participation in and completion of smoking-cessation programs."

The results of this study showed that financial incentives for smoking cessation significantly increased the rates of smoking cessation.

Modest financial rewards have a role to play in assisting behavior change as opposed to higher amounts that may in fact influence participation solely to obtain the money, rather than creating any lasting health transformation. These rewards will therefore be flexible and spread over the course of a program, rather than given as a lump sum. Dripping the incentive through the program, increasing it as the program nears completion, or for a progress achieved, or a variety of goals and challenges attained, are some of the individual methods that are a successful application of incentives. Also, spreading rewards throughout the length of a program will sustain momentum and encourage ongoing involvement. The art of motivating through the use of incentives takes many forms and this requires the incentives to be flexible and employ additional methods, as is found in tangible and intangible rewards which are discussed later in this chapter.

Programs, however, need not solely be targeted towards individuals. Group activities and departmental teams can, for example, be offered incentives with rewards given for groups who lose the most weight, or reducing the percentage of employees who smoke by 10 percent, or the team that walks the most steps. These are often short-term activities with immediate rewards and can help drive momentum, rather than using interventions that see slow results over many months.

You are making progress as you help to Generate Wins!

## Types Of Incentives

The budgetary aspect of your wellness program will have been decided and approved during the earlier planning stage, with resources allocated to implementing initial programs, in addition to incentives and the number of employees targeted. Likewise, the culture of your organization and employee demographics will also define the types of incentives that are appropriate or viable.

However, not all incentives are financial. There are a number of resources that are free such as publicly sponsored educational material and screenings, walking or running groups, and some family activities. These free or low-cost activities can also have an impact on motivation and behavior just like the higher monetized rewards. Incentives are designed to encourage participation, and their use may encourage short or long-term change, depending on their frequency, purpose and whether they are a personal or group incentive.

Achievements should always be recognized as employees succeed in reaching milestones on their path to improved wellness. Small things like a certificate of achievement are fun to hand out when in a group setting or during a celebration lunch to mark individuals reaching a three or six month milestone, in addition to marking the completion of a program.

Additionally, the type of incentive needs to match or be relevant to the activity or intervention. Many incentives will correspond naturally with the activity, such as discounts to attend an exercise class, thereby creating a direct association between participation and the reward, however all incentives need to be offered in conjunction with a reasonable timeframe to complete the goals.

**Points System**

A points system has advantages and disadvantages in terms of implementation, tracking, and evaluation and can be initiated to include the employee, their spouse and family, or partner. The incentives are typically financial, however they can also include sports equipment, and smaller items such as reserved parking spaces, discounts, and T-shirts. Positive lifestyle choices and activities are rewarded through points that are allocated to activities and the more points that an employee gathers, the higher their financial reward. With a points system, determine the points that will be allocated to each activity, and have a variety of incentives that can be acquired with accumulated points. Ensure that the updated list of incentives is sent on a regular predetermined basis, such as monthly or quarterly, to all employees. For example:

| POINTS INCENTIVE PROGRAM | | | |
|---|---|---|---|
| Employee Name: | | | |
| DATE | ACTIVITY | POINTS | POINTS EARNED |
| | Completion of a Health Assessment | 100 | |
| | Reduction in cholesterol level | 75 | |
| | Mammogram or prostate screening | 50 | |

| | | | |
|---|---|---|---|
| | Online coaching | 50 | |
| | Colon screening | 50 | |
| | Flu shot | 25 | |
| | Strength exercise 3 + times per week | 25 | |
| | Cardiovascular exercise 3 + times per week | 25 | |
| | Weekly stress management activities | 10 | |
| | Attending weekly lunch and learn | 10 | |
| | Walking outdoors daily | 10 | |

A benefits provider can also fund the points system, with rewards given out annually at the end of a year in return for proof that the activity took place for the desired length of time. Organizations can be incentivized through the points system too, obtaining a percentage reduction in premiums if employees reach an agreed number of points.

The points that an employee has to earn in order to obtain an incentive will typically increase annually as they become fitter and healthier. This has the advantage of encouraging employees to continue to reach to be their highest and best self. If for some reason an employee is struggling to gather points due to health reasons, the incentives program must be flexible enough to address this and provide other activities where an individual or family can obtain points. Remember, all aspects of the wellness program must be inclusive and available to all employees.

Research suggests that financial incentives alone are insufficient at maintaining long-term changes to health behaviors and indicate that other inducements such as identification of personal goals and application of intrinsic motivating factors need to be considered. Rewards fall into two categories:

1. Extrinsic or tangible incentives
2. Intrinsic or intangible incentives

**Extrinsic Motivation**

Let's examine extrinsic motivation (EM) and its rewards first. With this type of endeavor, the motivation to perform an activity and its subsequent reward comes from the reward itself. The external reinforcement can be physical, such as obtaining money or a trophy, or psychological as in obtaining praise or recognition amongst one's peers and managers and not from a deep personal desire. The reason for participation is therefore external and may not provide long-lasting behavior change, despite the fact that an individual is actively seen to be joining in and completing tasks. An individual who is motivated in this way will still derive satisfaction from completing a task, however it is the underlying reason for their participation that will define why they are involved and what type of reward best suits an individual.

An article in the American Psychological Society, January 2005, Vol 36, No1 by Zak Stambor examined a research study of 245 female students at a Belgian teacher training college between the ages of 19 and 20 years. They were tasked with reading instructions about recycling issues related to benefits for future toddlers and divided into three groups; future-extrinsic goals, future-intrinsic goals, and a double goal combining both future-extrinsic and future-intrinsic goals. The future-extrinsic group were told the recycling information would show them how they would save money by recycling, the future-intrinsic group were told the information would tell them how to teach toddlers to keep the environment clean, while the double group were told the information would do both, i.e. help them teach how to keep the environment clean and save money. Of the three groups, the students who were intrinsically motivated were the best at recalling the information, with the extrinsic group the worst. The double group also scored low and researchers believe that the extrinsic goal actually hampered the learning process, rather than making it more attainable, by shifting the focus externally and detracting from the goal of learning and comprehension. One of the researchers, Vansteenkiste, stated "Offering fewer goals to increase the relevance of learning is sometimes better, depending on the type and contents of goals." They concluded that when it comes to motivation, less is more.

When extrinsic rewards interfere with intrinsic motivation, this is referred to as the "over-justification effect." This occurs, for example, when the extrinsic reward is so lavish that there is no interest in continuing with the activity when the extrinsic reward is removed. Likewise, extrinsic motivation can seem like effort and hard work and the reward has to reflect the perceived effort demanded.

Extrinsic incentives typically involve monetary discounts, coupons, trophies and medals, or merchandise such as gym-bags and fitness clothing with flexible usage in their applications. They can be offered for a variety of behaviors including signing-up, completion of a task, or reaching specific goals. While these can be an effective EM tool, the rewards should be small in value and linked directly to a specific task in order to foster ongoing interest in continuing with a program, or participating in another one.

Extrinsic incentives are not without their disadvantages though. To some employees, certain material items can be viewed as gimmicky or cheap and not worth the effort of participation and certainly not something they want to wear or display on their desk. Extrinsic rewards also have to fit in with the corporate culture and tailored to suit the recipients. In addition to costs, there is also the issue of time spent selecting the items, difficulty with storage, possible expiry dates, and the cost of forwarding to employees in other offices or their home.

**Examples of Extrinsic Incentives**

| EXTRINSIC REWARD | VALUE | DISADVANTAGE |
|---|---|---|
| Payment of program or gym fees. | Given at completion of an exercise program or annual gym membership. | Reduced motivation due to length of duration between starting and completing program. |
| Merchandise. Hats, T-shirts, mugs etc. | Wellness program branding, inexpensive, suitable for team-building. | Limited ongoing use, low visibility. |
| Elite Services. | Pampering and privileged access to events and luxury | Limited use if only for one person, rather than offering two passes. |

| | | |
|---|---|---|
| | activities. Can be low cost if a donated service or pass. | |
| Waiver of pre-existing condition. | Linked to the Health plan. | The initial value to the employee may decline over time. |
| Bonus for Medical Savings account. | Useful for anticipated medical expenses. | May not be fully utilized. It is a one-off payment. |
| Time off. Immediate. | Generally popular. Can be used to suit employees' personal needs. Non-taxable. | Value diminishes on whether employee is part or full-time and amount of vacation time allowed. |
| Time off. Delayed. | Generally popular. Can be used to suit employees' personal needs. Non-taxable. | Demotivating due to length of time between reward and taking time off. |
| Gift Cards. | A popular reward. | Taxable income. |
| Cash. Immediate. | Highest incentive. | Taxable income therefore cash-in-hand is less. |
| Cash at end of intervention. | Opportunity to have a higher monetary reward than immediate cash. | Can lose interest, as reward is too distant. Taxable income therefore cash-in-hand is less. |

## Intrinsic Motivation

Intrinsic Motivation (IM) is what drives each of us to do something for personal satisfaction, instead of an external reward such as money. This self-motivated desire flows from within and drives an individual to engage in a task, or pursue a goal with enthusiasm, because it is interesting and enjoyable. However, IM also works alongside the external tangible benefits such as one's professional role and having a good salary, generating a workforce that enjoys work-life balance, job satisfaction with one's tasks, appreciation for activities completed, and challenging assignments. Dissatisfied employees do not feel they are realizing their potential; they feel a lack of communication or that their work lacks purpose. These emotions increase stress on the individual, place limitations on their ability to perform their daily work well, resulting in a disengaged worker who eventually leaves the company, which increases recruitment costs.

An article by Kenneth Thomas in the November/December 2009 issue of the Ivey Business Journal *"The Four Intrinsic Rewards That Drive Employee Engagement"* emphasized the importance of IM in the workplace and in particular the new "models and strategies that better reflect the changes in today's work dynamics." The following extract highlights the response of employees to today's work environment and how they:

"add value—innovating, problem solving and improvizing to meet the conditions they encounter to meet customers' needs. The self-management process involves four key steps:

1. Committing to a meaningful purpose
2. Choosing the best way of fulfilling that purpose
3. Making sure that one is performing work activities competently

4. Making sure that one is making progress to achieving the purpose

Each of these steps requires workers to make a judgment—about the meaningfulness of their purpose, the degree of *choice* they have for doing things the right way, the competence of their performance, and the actual progress being made toward fulfilling the purpose."

Kenneth Thomas further suggests that each of these steps, or reasons, is accompanied by an emotional response and he describes the four intrinsic rewards as follows:

1. Sense of **meaningfulness**. This reward involves the meaningfulness or importance of the purpose you are trying to fulfill. You feel that you have an opportunity to accomplish something of real value—something that matters in the larger scheme of things. You feel that you are on a path that is worth your time and energy, giving you a strong sense of purpose or direction.

2. Sense of **choice**. You feel free to choose how to accomplish your work—to use your best judgment to select those work activities that make the most sense to you and to perform them in ways that seem appropriate. You feel ownership of your work, believe in the approach you are taking, and feel responsible for making it work.

3. Sense of **competence**. You feel that you are handling your work activities well—that your performance of these activities meets or exceeds your personal standards, and that you are doing good, high-quality work. You feel a sense

of satisfaction, pride, or even artistry in how well you handle these activities.

4. Sense of **progress**. You are encouraged that your efforts are really accomplishing something. You feel that your work is on track and moving in the right direction. You see convincing signs that things are working out, giving you confidence in the choices you have made and confidence in the future."

Connectivity is enhanced by valuing an employee's contribution and through visible support from their manager. In turn, motivated employees enjoy their work and promote the company and its products passionately to friends as a great place to work.

## The Benefits Of Intrinsic Motivation

The benefits of IM for both the individual and the company include:

| Work-life balance | Self-determination |
|---|---|
| Increased focus | Low-cost to implement |
| Perceived control | Increased well-being and reduced burn-out |
| Improved staff-retention | Enhanced morale |

Long-term sustainability arises through implementing policy changes and incorporating coaching, Intrinsic Motivation, incentives, and the conditions mentioned earlier to personalize plans, create a sense of purpose and belonging, and build a culture of engagement to manifest significant results and commitment.

IM is therefore a valuable tool with rewards for employers and employees. By encouraging participation in the decision-making process it also becomes self-sustaining and empowers individuals to feel that they are making a worthy contribution. This creates a performance-driven cycle of positive reinforcement. Built from the top down, IM fosters growth and progress through specific steps. The results are trust, engagement, and significantly higher job satisfaction, which in turn reduces the perception of stress and allows employees to manage work-life conflicts better.

- Wellness programs with IM will not only strengthen what is working but help drive the momentum forward to enable the organization to achieve its goals.
- Work-life balance initiatives and IM add to the skills of managers by helping them enable team members to achieve work-life balance for a minimum investment, thus benefiting the organization and employees.
- IM is a structured approach, tailored to the needs of the company and is an investment in the employees. In addition, consultants, those on assignment, and non-office based employees will also have an opportunity to experience the benefits of IM, thereby cultivating the corporate culture of shared values.

**Examples Of Intrinsic Incentives**

| INTRINSIC REWARD | VALUE | DISADVANTAGE |
|---|---|---|
| Recognition. | Low cost with photographs, certificates, and company-wide | Limited use in small companies. Must vary the individuals or teams who are |

| | email. Motivates other employees. | recognized. |
|---|---|---|
| Community Player. | Membership of an exclusive club. Clothing that shows belonging to special group. | Not of value to every employee. May disincentivize or alienate some employees. |
| President's Club Resort Conference attendee with management. | High-profile. Usually abroad in a luxury hotel. Partner is often invited. | Reward may lessen if partner is not included. May be intimidating for some employees. |
| Advanced training or certification in a skill the employee wishes to enhance. | This can be a personal, creative, or health skill or it can be a work-related skill such as training in public speaking. | Can be challenging to complete creating an adverse reaction to further participation. |
| Volunteering. | Low-cost, creates positive energy regarding self and organization. | Can involve large numbers of employees and thus challenging to organize. |

## Group Incentives

The psychology behind group incentives combines the need to identify and belong to a team, combined with elements of competition and rewards. The incentives can be offered for activities such as participation in, as well as completion of, a task or winning a team competition. These activities and their rewards can also be a blend of extrinsic and intrinsic rewards including team-building, rapport, and increased motivation. Group incentives also provide the wellness team with an additional variety of activities and incentives. Some disadvantages of group or team incentives include the pressure to participate by unwilling employees, or resentment towards team members or opposing teams.

So how can managers build a culture of engagement and foster IM in their team setting?

Providing coaching for managers enables them to first identify their own intrinsic motivation factors i.e. what is personally meaningful, and what skills they need to develop within themselves, so that they will better understand the dynamics of Intrinsic Motivation and the steps required to gauge growth in their team.

Support for managers comes in a variety of inputs and resources that will help them make the wellness program a success. Intrinsic coaching is an important factor in developing and managing a workforce who are engaged and enthusiastic about being at their place of work. Managers can encourage their team by developing intrinsic rewards through simple methods such as "Fido Friday" where employees in a small office can bring their dog to work (providing everyone loves dogs), or encouraging team members to share their knowledge of a subject in a short presentation to peers at team meetings. For employees, this can promote feelings of competence, ownership, and self-assurance. Other mediums for supporting managers with wellness program responsibilities include regular peer meetings, trainings,

HR updates on benefits and policies, and support from executive coaches who specialize in wellness.

A positive feedback system will not only evaluate, it will allow management to adapt, formulate recommendations for improvements, and manage change. Through monitoring and endorsing activities, developing a sense of meaning and purpose to projects, and providing scope to participate, managers can build a powerful team that thrives on producing great results, is satisfied with accomplishing work that is valued, and proud to make a difference.

When managers highlight what is working well within their team and the organization, this instills a sense that more is going well. It paves the way to explore what motivates each member of their team, helping individuals to engage in constructive levels of challenge, and look at additional steps that can be taken to foster rewards such as areas of self-growth and success in attaining personal goals. This team becomes an example of a highly-engaged workforce that is empowered and motivated.

## Motivation And Engagement

Motivation and engagement overlap which is why coaching bridges the gap between needs, incentives, motivation, and ultimately engagement. Coaching programs provide a new direction for managers and team leaders to acknowledge and balance their own personal and professional objectives and recognize and address the needs of the employees. Combined with Intrinsic Motivation, coaching blends the diversity of skills and cultures within the company and addresses the question of "Who is mentoring the managers?" Coaching directed towards employees is discussed more fully in chapter six.

# Building A Culture Of Engagement Through Executive Coaching

- Executive coaching enables mangers to identify the role of their own intrinsic motivation, i.e. what is meaningful, what skills do they need to develop within themselves so that they will better understand its importance and manage it in others, and the steps required to gauge growth in their team.

- A positive feedback system will not only evaluate, it will allow management to adapt, formulate recommendations for improvements, and manage change. Through monitoring and reinforcing activities, developing a sense of meaning and purpose to projects, and providing scope to participate, managers can build a powerful team that thrives on producing great results, is satisfied with accomplishing work that is valued, and proud to make a difference.

- When managers highlight what is working well, what may have been over-looked, and instill a sense that all is going well, this enables them to build on this steady foundation by exploring what motivates their team, helping them to engage in constructive levels of challenge, and look at additional steps that can be taken to foster additional rewards such as self-growth and success in attaining personal goals. This group becomes an example of a highly-engaged workforce that is empowered and motivated.

## Wellness Budget

With all of the variables related to the types of incentives and their relationship to the activities and interventions, gauging the costs and calculating a budget requires strong data on the types of interventions that are planned, the number of employees that are involved, if extra staff are required to implement the interventions, what a reasonable and/or legally permissible incentive is possible based on the constraints of the operating plan and budget, and even whether the incentive is monthly, or annual from a cash-flow perspective. All of the parameters, when known, have to also be factored in to estimating the potential and actual return on investment (ROI).

As you can see from the example of incentives listed previously, some incentives have a nominal cost associated with them; others are annual costs, while others may be incentivized via an outside source like a benefits provider. Additionally, there are other items that need to be factored in when gauging the costs:

- The type of activity
- The length of time that it will be implemented
- The number of employees expected to participate
- Whether it is an onsite or off-site facility
- The type of equipment used

A typical wellness program will offer a variety of interventions throughout the year and the incentives will also vary, when applicable, in response to the program models that will be in place. The cost of providing an incentive will be added into the total cost of each corresponding intervention and the number of employees targeted. This will give a total price per employee per year.

Monetized incentives and gift cards may be considered taxable items, whether given to the employee or a family member. This information also needs to be conveyed to employees and factored in when budgeting, as the organization needs to decide whether an incentive warrants withholding of taxes related to the value of the reward. Services by certified professionals will also accrue additional costs and need to be factored in to the wellness budget plan.

## Incentives Communication

"Build it and they will come." This may have worked in the movie *Field of Dreams*, however a clear exchange of information is necessary between employees and the wellness team to ensure there is adequate program awareness. In order to attain a reward, the employee needs to know what they have to do to achieve a particular incentive, therefore the communication plan must make sure that all materials conform to the wellness program brand, integrates the feedback from employees, and delivers information pertinent to the wellness programs.

Ultimately this requires a clear and straightforward explanation about what needs to be completed, what the timeframe is, and what the reward is. The information should also be repeated early and frequently and posted in a variety of mediums such as a corporate newsletter, testimonials, success stories, social sites, intranet, emails, posters displayed in high-traffic areas, and Q&A sessions etc. to ensure a clear understanding of what is required by participants.

An informal survey or small group meeting, for example, will uncover what types of incentives employees would prefer, such as cash, paid time off, movie tickets, or tickets to a sporting event. There is no right or wrong answer here, it is merely an exploratory session to discover what employees find motivating to them. Then, based upon the budget and operating plan, incentives can be woven in to the benefits strategy and the various health programs that will be offered.

Ultimately, whatever method of communication is used, the message should be well-defined, demonstrate how easy it is to participate, and be accessible.

**Designing A Three-Year Wellness Incentive Plan**

As the health and fitness of employees improves, the wellness program should offer harder challenges each year that employees and their families can participate in. The Three-Year Wellness Incentive Plan will comprise multiple objectives and activities that overlap throughout each year, supporting participation, achievement towards interim personal goals, and a larger incentive for attaining the main goal. It will encompass the goals and objectives, the type of incentive program i.e. participation only or one that requires a health modification, all of the proposed interventions, activities, educational programs, and all of the incentives to be offered. Pace the incentives and diversify the types of rewards that you offer by having a grand prize supported with smaller prizes along the way, tailoring the incentives to suit the demographics of your population. The following table uses S.M.A.R.T. objectives and examples of incentives that could be used with a particular intervention.

135

Decide on the type of incentive program your organization with adopt i.e. participation only, such as regular attendance at an approved fitness center, or one that requires a health modification where employees must meet specific requirements to qualify for an incentive such as nutritional changes, percentage of weight loss, or reaching preset fitness goals.

Other options include assigning participation points that can be reimbursed for incentive rewards.

|  | GOAL | INTERVENTION | INCENTIVE |
|---|---|---|---|
| **Year 1** | Introduce HRA. | Complete HRA. New employees to complete HRA. | $100 gift cards to complete HRA. |
|  | Create a healthy environment. Offer on-site health education classes and tips to lower stress. | Show prompt appreciation to employees. Survey to determine short and long term stressors. Provide financial counseling. | Free personal coaching of the employees choice. Offer free weekly onsite yoga/meditation classes. |
|  | Reduce the number of employees who are overweight. | Provide educational resources to establish healthy nutritional habits for employees and their families to lower BMI by 10% (within healthy parameters). Provide weight management support groups. | Provide food-tracking plan. Provide meal planning with a dietician. |
|  | Appraise vending food and beverage machine | Offer healthy vending options and educational lunch and learn sessions to | Subsidize healthy foods in vending machines. |

|  |  |  |  |
| --- | --- | --- | --- |
|  | selections. | support weight reduction. | Provide lunch boxes.<br>Free 12-week course with a weight management vendor. |
|  | Create physical programs. | Initiate daily lunchtime walking groups. | Fitness center reimbursement. |
|  | Reduce number of smokers by 50%. | Offer smoking cessation aids to participants such as patches, education, and support classes. Provide group coaching. Develop and implement tobacco policies. | $50 monthly insurance premium discount to employees who do not use tobacco products. |
| **Year 2** | Complete HRA. | Team competition to encourage completion of HRA. | $125 gift cards for completion of HRA.<br>Bonus for team who finishes first. |
|  | Increase health fair participation. | Promotion of health fair via intranet and posters. | Gift cards for attending the health fair. |
|  | Create a relaxed environment. Provide weekly lunch and learn programs on lowering stress. | Have a weekly comedy DVD during Friday lunchtime, or share vacation pictures. Time-management course. Implement stretching sessions and policies to ensure regular | Personalize promotional wellness items such as yoga mat bags, monogramed towels, sports clothing, or water bottles. |

| | | | |
|---|---|---|---|
| | | breaks | |
| | Appraise cafeteria meals. Offer nutrition programs. Increase the number of physical programs. | Provide on-site weight-loss programs.<br><br>Add basketball hoops in an outdoor area. | Offer discounts for external weight-loss programs.<br><br>Provide pedometers, bicycle mileage trackers, sports equipment. |
| | Increase smoking cessation attempts. | Provide smoking cessation education and coaching. | $50 monthly insurance premium discount to employees who do not use tobacco products. |
| **Year 3** | Complete HRA. | Promotion of HRA via intranet and posters. | $150 gift cards for completion of HRA. An additional $50 if the employee's department has 85% or greater participation in HRA. |
| | Achieve 70% participation at health fair. | Use intranet and team participation challenges to highlight the fair. | Gift cards for attending the health fair. |
| | Lower stress through flexi-time work plan. | Introduce flexi-time. Develop and implement policies to support flexi-time. Sleep management course. | Reduced fees for fitness and yoga classes. |

| | | | |
|---|---|---|---|
| | Educate employees on healthy eating and disease prevention. | Have a "zero" competition between Thanksgiving and New Year. The challenge is to not gain any weight during this period. | A "members only" lunch for employees who successfully achieve a physical challenge. |
| | Increase the difficulty of physical challenges. | Day field trips with a physical trainer to hone skills. | Company-paid entry fees to competitions. |
| | Eliminate smoking at workplace. | Provide smoking cessation education and coaching. | Reduced deductible for completely stopping tobacco usage. |

A great deal of thought needs to go into the incentive plan to ensure compliance with government regulations, to have a plan that is flexible, and to have incentives that work with the goal and the activity that will support wellness and positive lifestyle behavior change. It also provides a good tool when you are ready to perform annual program evaluations.

**Review Checklist**
1. Create an incentive program plan
2. Check that everyone has an opportunity to participate in the programs
3. Determine if the incentive plan is likely to drive behavior change
4. Include intrinsic motivational factors
5. Put a plan in place to review the three-year strategy annually
6. Apply incentive amounts over several categories

7. Ensure the incentive design rewards positive modifications in health
8. Determine how you will encourage employees to participate in the first intervention
9. Generate wins, recognize contributions and celebrate all victories, big and small

# CHAPTER 6

## Step 6: Development

*Expanding The Wellness Program.*

Maintaining interest and enthusiasm for the wellness program as a whole means that you will need to identify where and how you will build, grow, and expand your programs. New areas of expansion will require the ongoing support of executive leadership and follow each of the seven steps of implementation and growth of a wellness program in order to continue to nurture an environment of change and foster a workplace culture that embraces health in all its facets.

### Building On Existing Programs

Physical and nutritional programs lend themselves to expansion relatively easily. Their development can be as simple, for example, as adding educational elements to the nutritional programs with guest speakers at lunchtime who can expand existing nutrition programs by providing recipes or delivering a talk on how to incorporate healthy food choices at work and at home. Spread over a few weeks, these new and basic features keep the enthusiasm and momentum going.

Educational events are frequently a natural progression of the original programs and can be expanded further by taking a broader perspective. For example, the physical program can be expanded with the addition of foosball tables, or chair massage sessions for individuals who reach a goal, which can lead to adding stress-reduction interventions including:

- Meditation classes
- "Fido-Fridays" in small offices with dog-loving employees and well-trained dogs
- Relaxation workshops
- Sleep (fatigue) management; getting a better night's sleep without medication

Each of these in turn can spark other spin-off programs and interventions. Sleep management research, for example, is showing a correlation between lack of, or poor quality, sleep and an increased risk of heart disease, obesity, diabetes, and other diseases. Additionally, wellness programs related to sleep management can target the root causes of poor sleep including medical conditions, physical environment, alcohol use, and lifestyle habits.

By combining an evidence-based approach to wellness with knowledge of what your employees want, you can be creative and tailor programs to include interventions such as:

- Financial guidance and planning
- Assistance with caring for a senior family member
- Planning for college for teens

## Wellness Month

A designated wellness month allows the wellness team to showcase new and invigorating elements and generate lots of interest and action around wellness. This can be held annually or twice a year, e.g. summer and winter, and offer a variety of seasonal activities and lively events such as:

- Team competitions for bowling
- Skiing and cross-country winter activities
- Volunteering around town at local food banks or charities
- Golfing sessions

Be creative with how you present or offer each activity. For example, bringing in a sports' professional usually results in high participation as people sign up to play golf, tennis, or other form of sport and are then evaluated by the instructor. Lunchtime can also be enlivened by inviting martial arts professionals to put on a live performance or by bringing in therapists such as acupuncturists who explain the history of their profession, the types of ailments that they treat, and then proceed to give a demonstration where an assistant experiences a brief acupuncture session. These are often fun and interactive presentations that augment the program as a whole.

Additional topics for a wellness month include:

- Visits by local organic vendors to supply local produce weekly that can also be ordered in advance
- Deliver daily inspirational messages and wellness information via emails and the company intranet

- Share success stories with photographs of achievers posted in a designated area and intranet

The ideas list is huge and the team can have fun brainstorming and implementing the plan during a whole month that is dedicated to a variety of aspects of health that are fun, get people moving, and stimulate interest in the vendors and volunteering events. The team can both kick the month off and end it with a healthy breakfast in a common area to encourage networking.

**Coaching To Succeed**

Coaching is a powerful tool and can be tailored to suit any of the cornerstone programs. In the previous chapter, coaching was introduced and now we'll explore the benefits in more detail. A professional coach takes a holistic approach to wellness and meets the employee wherever they are on their path to wellness. They guide employees to achieve goals in areas such as work-life balance, stress-management, better nutrition and weight reduction, fitness, tobacco cessation, or achieving better overall health. Coaching is built on trust, encourages and empowers individuals, helps them to build lasting skills, and enables not only office-based employees to achieve key results, but employees in the field too. This expert approach is not a "quick-fix" but a program that offers steady growth, measurable accomplishments, and lasting change. There is individual accountability in making progress through an appropriate timescale and personal realistic goals.

Professional coaches adhere to the guidelines set by the International Coaching Federations, are certified in health and/or wellness, fitness, business, and may have additional qualifications such as nursing, physical therapy, or nutrition. They are dedicated to empowering people to discover self-efficacy and develop a "Can Do" attitude by listening compassionately and non-judgmentally, through the use of supportive language, enquiring and communication methods, and positive reinforcement. This creative approach facilitates change by helping individuals to positively reframe obstacles, to tap into their inner strengths, and ultimately realize what motivates them. Even when there are perceived failures, the positive reframing of situations by the coach shows that there is always something to cheer for. The coach works collaboratively with employees to explore what has happened and helps them to see how they can recognize and prevent similar situations. It is often necessary to stress to employees that their work with a coach is always confidential.

During the life of a coaching program, growth and change will occur at different rates and sometimes progress is highly evident and consistent and at other times slow. Through each stage, a coach will work with the employee and assist them in uncovering their strengths and abilities, and help them to set realistic goals. For the employee, having someone who believes in them and that they have what it takes to succeed is huge. This, in turn, sets up a solid foundation to develop realistic goals, strategies, and ultimately achieve success. The benefits of coaching programs for both the individual and the company include:

| Developing trust and growth with employees | Low-cost to implement |
|---|---|
| Employee engagement | Attracting and retaining employees |
| More energy - less stress | Greater well-being |

| Knowing when to unplug from work and have personal time | Fostering an environment of creativity and teamwork |
| --- | --- |

Coaching can and often does dig deep to uncover deep-seated habits that the individual may not be aware of, yet these entrenched behaviors are frequently creating the wellness issues. This indicates that coaching is not a quick fix, but it does deliver lasting change by building a professional partnership that focuses on encouragement, rather than giving advice or solving problems, and by helping the employee to uncover their current practices and work towards lifestyle changes. Ultimately, participants in coaching will set new and more challenging goals in the knowledge that they have the skills to not only achieve them, but to counter and positively reframe any obstacles that occur. This is an important distinction as self-efficacy is key in helping an individual to make lasting progress by seeing and experiencing ways that they can overcome perceived barriers to their health, thereby strengthening their belief in themselves.

### Self-Efficacy

Each one of us is unique, with a different life-story that impacts our choices, reactions, and path in life. Our experiences contribute to our belief in our abilities to perform specific actions, to follow through on our objectives and attain our goals. Self-efficacy is explained in the model of Social Cognitive Theory written by Albert Bandura, and is defined by the American Psychological Association as "an individual's belief in his or her capacity to execute behaviors necessary to produce specific performance attainments. Self-efficacy reflects confidence in the ability to exert control over one's own motivation, behavior, and social environment."

Note that self-esteem is very different from self-efficacy. Self-esteem, while providing a person with confidence and self-worth, is not necessarily impacted by the belief that they can or cannot do a particular activity, nor does having high self-esteem affect self-efficacy and the ability to reach for or attain goals. General confidence does spread positivity and resilience and is therefore an important factor in providing a firm base for self-efficacy.

Self-efficacy is important, as people have to know how to care for themselves and have a reason and/or purpose for wanting to make a life change. Self-efficacy makes change not only possible, but increases the likelihood of lasting and positive change occurring.

In his 1997 book, *Self-Efficacy: The Exercise Of Control*, Bandura explores four areas that impact self-efficacy: cognitive, motivational, affective, and selection processes. Let's take a brief look at each of these areas and how they relate to wellness programs and impact a person's ability to foster the desire to want to learn new skills, to set new goals, and develop positive changes.

- **Cognitive Process:** When an individual has a high level of belief in their ability to perform a certain task, they set more challenging goals for themselves. In addition, their commitment level to achieving these goals is strong. However, conveying positive affirmations in an individual's ability to succeed must be realistic otherwise they are being set up for failure. Encouragement should be given to strengthen commitment and effort and in this way, self-belief becomes strengthened and self-efficacy increases.

- **Motivational Process:** Self-belief is a positive cognitive thought process and the ability to self-motivate can produce a powerful determination to succeed, and also signify to others that they too can be like this person and be successful at realizing their own similar objective. Additionally, this impacts self-efficacy as it reinforces inner strength and perseverance through realizing one's ability to conquer a perceived hurdle.
- **Affective Process:** Control over negative thoughts and the confidence to overcome adverse experiences results in an individual who feels positive towards change and is relaxed and stress-free.
- **Selection Process:** Beliefs are shaped by multiple social factors that exert an influence over an individual's beliefs, values, and perceived abilities long after the initial experience has occurred. The more positive, rewarding, and challenging experiences that an individual has, such as succeeding at achieving a desired goal, the more the experiences go on to create a positive mind-set. However the successes need to be both attainable and challenging, otherwise an individual can become bored or consistently fail and in turn lose self-belief and ultimately self-efficacy.

Achieving success through their own determination, skills, and effort bolsters the desire to change and set attainable realistic goals, subsequently giving an individual the motivation and confidence to share their success stories with others. This generates a

"Can Do" attitude amongst colleagues and social networks.

### Recognition

Many organizations know the value of using recognition and rewards as a means of supporting and encouraging employees, and recognition is a powerful wellness program tool when it is used successfully, happens regularly, aligns with the branding of the program and culture of the company, and integrates a variety of methods.

According to a 2009 global recognition survey by Towers Watson, *Turbocharging Employee Engagement*, the act of recognizing performance can increase employee engagement by up to 60 percent, particularly so when the recognition is delivered by their direct line manager. However, the survey showed that managers only had a favorable score of 56 percent in recognizing and appreciating employees.

Take a look at your own company and determine the level of general recognition that is currently taking place. Is the balance right? Does your company have an effective recognition program with managers and employees taking an active role in recognizing co-workers? If necessary, conduct an anonymous survey amongst managers and employees to find out what types and frequency of recognition is being done and what additional acknowledgement they would like to see happen. Does more work and training need to be done in this area to stress the importance of recognition and to train managers in particular in delivering recognition? Having a solid recognition plan in place is therefore important when applying recognition to wellness too.

Recognition is closely intertwined with employee engagement and just as the wellness program offers a variety of events and interventions in order to meet the needs of employees and addresses the different ways that people learn, it should also provide a variety of meaningful ways that people can be recognized and rewarded. Additionally, timing is important and recognition should be given as close to the achievement of the actual event or goal that is being rewarded.

Generally, recognition is often employed to acknowledge personal growth and achievement, leading by example, or a team success, however within the realms of a wellness program, recognition can take many forms and can be a strong motivating influence in encouraging specific behavior change.

Recognition is frequently based on actual results such as losing ten pounds towards a target weight, or walking 10,000 steps every day for 10 weeks. It can also be directed towards individuals or groups who participate in a wellness activity rather than solely achieving a specific milestone. Rewarding specific wellness behavior not only says "thank you" or "well-done" to the person or team who achieved their goal, it sends a message to the organization that the person is doing the right thing and that the effort is appreciated. This expresses the significance of recognition, the importance of its value, and further fosters a cycle of motivation and encouragement.

Types of recognition include:
- Tangible awards: trophies, medals, certificates
- Recognition Wall
- Employee of the month
- Cash
- Gift certificates

- Signed book
- Recognition event off campus

While these are similar to incentives, they are given upon completion of an event and reflect the effort put into it. There are also the intangible rewards tied into public recognition:

- Appreciation
- Peer-to-peer recognition
- Department specific recognition
- Recognition for community volunteering

Peer-to-peer recognition is often influential; as one's direct colleagues know what a person does on a day-to-day basis. The renowned psychologist Frederick Herzberg wrote, *"True motivation comes from achievement, personal development, job satisfaction, and recognition."*

Recognition is an aid to staff retention, can be used during the hiring process to highlight the value that the company places on individuals and team effort, and strengthens the wellness program brand as a whole.

**The Health Fair**

A health/wellness fair comprises many opportunities for discussing health and wellness with your employees and should be informative, educational, and fun with numerous events and activities to participate in. The terms health or wellness are interchangeable depending on the branding of your wellness program and the wellness team should determine which term best suits the culture of your organization. For ease of continuity and comprehension, the term "health fair" is used in this section. The topics that you cover will be influenced by the demographics of your employees, whether or not spouses and partners are included, and the general needs of your organization. This means that you may decide that you are going to run a large all-day event off-site with multiple vendors, state services, and screenings and activities or choose to have a simpler half-day event inside your company building offering only a couple of activities, a screening, flu shots, and updated benefits information. Be creative when planning the fair; perhaps have a festive atmosphere while incorporating your wellness brand and the corporate culture.

Depending on the size of your event, it can take four to eight months to plan the health fair so care must be taken to factor in the time that is being spent on programs that are currently taking place, the regular daily workload and availability of the team members who will be involved in developing the fair, and any other factors such as vacations as these may necessitate the fair taking longer to plan and implement. The fair is an annual event therefore once the first fair has been held all the lessons learned should be applied to future events.

Note: The health fair must also be treated in a similar manner to wellness program. For example, the health fair should be scheduled to overlap all shifts so that all employees can have the opportunity to attend and participate.

**Organizing The Health Fair**

The following steps provide an outline for organizing a health fair and can be scaled up or down depending on what type of event you want to offer the employees:

- **Form A Health Fair Planning Committee:** Staying aligned with the objectives of the overall wellness program, the health fair committee will organize and promote the fair while aiming for a high percentage of participation and sign-ups by employees.

- **Theme And Content:** Build the health fair around a specific topic to align with and maintain consistency and connection with the wellness program. Decide who the fair is aimed at; will it be only employees or will partners and families be included too. Consider tying in with a goal of the wellness program or a national health observance day.

- **Set Goals And Objectives**: These can include determining the level and type of education and screenings that you will provide, or the number of participants in a targeted health risk such as smoking that you want to sign up for a program during the health fair.

- **Invite Internal Volunteers:** Define the specific responsibilities and duties of the volunteers during both the organizing stage, a few days prior, and during the day of the fair. Typically, they will assist with setting and clearing up, escorting vendors into and out of the company or off-site location, and supervising sign-ups and evaluations.

- **Budget:** Factor in the costs of fees, promotional materials, prizes, and what can be obtained free of cost from vendors and donors.

- **Vendors:** Determine the type of vendors and any fees involved. Include a variety of skills and information, notify reception, and arrange clearance and visitor passes if special access is necessary or if there are equipment needs.

- **Blood Drive:** The American Red Cross will bring the equipment and supplies. Ensure that you provide chairs, tables, and of course refreshments.
- **Timeline:** Carefully calculate the length of time required for designing and printing promotional and publicity materials, factoring in the best availability dates of vendors, sending confirmation emails, phone calls, and pre-event meetings to event volunteers and vendors, researching and reserving a venue, and the weeks involved in marketing the health fair.
- **Logistics:** These include scheduling the best date, determining if the health fair is on-site or at an off-site location, designing a floor plan of where each vendor will be placed, checking logistics for access, organizing photography and videography, organizing a PA system, AV aids, tables, chairs, nametags, event bags, bunting, printing of material and posters, and healthy catering.
- **Promotion:** These resources will blend with the wellness program brand and will be used in promoting the fair to employees, vendors, donors, and as material for the media. A variety of methods for promotion and advertising will be used to encourage participation.
- **Thank You:** Send thank you correspondence to vendors, volunteers, and participants.
- **Evaluation:** Follow up with a one-page electronic survey to determine the favorability of the content, each provider, ideas for improvement, and the overall impression of the fair.

## Health Fair Activities

Successful fairs are engaging, informative and typically cover the following three areas: awareness, screenings, and demonstrations. Generally, the agenda will cover areas of concern to the needs of your organization such as breast or prostate screening, and provide information on the physical, nutritional, and tobacco cessation programs that are currently in place.

- **Awareness**:
  Self-examination
  Back health with presentation by a chiropractor
  Sun protection
  Cancer awareness and prevention
  Tobacco cessation
  Second-hand smoke
  Stress management
  Signs of a stroke
  Nutritional information
  Elder care information
  Pre-natal care
  Child health
  Chiropody
  Educational material
- **Screenings**:
  Blood pressure
  Hearing test
  Eye test
  Cholesterol test
- **Demonstrations**:
  Acupuncture
  Chiropractor
  Yoga
  Martial Arts
  Fitness equipment from a local gym

Cooking

Reiki and holistic therapies

Chair massage

CPR and First Aid

Dental care

Arthritis prevention

Ergonomics

Financial wellness presentation

How to lift properly

MADD (Mothers Against Drunk Driving)

Using green products at home

Safety at home

Fitting child car seats

Organic food producers; bread, fruits and vegetables

- **Miscellaneous**:

Role out new information on the EAP

Sign-ups for recreational events

Voluntary organizations looking for volunteers

Raffles

Quizzes and competitions

Scavenger hunt

Launch a fitness challenge

Launch a health challenge

Win a spa day

Refreshments

A successful health fair is informative, interactive, and appeals to both the large and small demographic areas of your workforce. The vendors will comprise a blend of non-profit organizations, community groups, and professional companies all of whom will cover an aspect of heath and wellbeing and contribute to an experience that is collaborative and appealing, rather than merely dry information served up in the form of brochures.

**Participation Versus Engagement**

All too often, the initial success of a program is based upon the number of attendees taking part in a particular event, however in reality it is not only participation that is important. Engagement and participation are often thought of in similar terms, yet the reasons for an employee being present during an intervention varies immensely and the reasons will ultimately make the difference between the program being something that one is simply seen to turn up to, to one that delivers lasting change. While incentives may encourage participation in the short term, intrinsic motivating factors trigger an emotional connection that motivates and engages an individual on a deep and personal level.

Engagement is an area that can impact not only the wellness program, but also an employee's relationship with their work. It can shape how they interact with their peers, influence their home and social environment, and affect their motivation to achieve organizational and personal goals. Low engagement is a constant drip that leads to dissatisfaction, low morale, and high turnover that ultimately impacts the bottom line.

With the majority of employees being physically well, a good wellness program covers a variety of dimensions of wellness of an individual's life, demonstrates to employees that their company cares about them enough to make the initial investment and that it is not just their productivity at work that matters to management, it is the employee as a whole person that counts. This can be actively demonstrated by organizing a specific "Family And Friends Day" to emphasize the importance of social and family involvement when it comes to taking care of one's health. This fun day can be held in a park where there are a variety of field events and games and it can include bike rides, hikes, and other outdoor family-friendly pursuits

These initiatives cover areas not typically associated with the workplace such as social, spiritual, emotional, and financial endeavors although they can have a negative impact on an organization if not adequately supported. Encouraging educational pursuits related to furthering an individual's career is good for both the employee and the organization. If a motivated and career-driven employee has no opportunities or occupational goals to pursue, they will most likely leave and pursue them elsewhere.

A program that uses a holistic approach addressing all aspects of an employee's life has a greater chance of success as programs overlap between home and work. Motivation and engagement increase due to the ongoing support for growth creating a win-win situation for all parties involved.

To facilitate engagement within the parameters of the wellness program, the wellness team has to connect with the employees through accurate knowledge of needs, by aligning the needs with the goals of the program and the organization, and by working with managers to identify the intrinsic motivating factors of individuals or their team as a whole. This requires solid listening and communication skills, combined with an openness and willingness to provide programs that promote real benefits to the individual. When this happens, employees are more likely to feel at ease at their company and recommend their organization and its products to friends and family. Retention increases and employees become more engaged with their work and their environment.

### Communications Campaign

Prior to the implementation of a wellness program, the wellness team will promote, promote, promote, however successfully maximizing participation relies upon a communications campaign that does more than spread information about upcoming events.

A strong communications campaign will highlight individual and group achievements through a variety of methods, such as newsletters, email, and video content on your intranet. These provide multiple opportunities to share information and the wellness successes within your organization. The purpose of this campaign is to provide the wellness team with another tool to drive program participation, to proclaim loudly about who has achieved a particular objective, and to publicly recognizes employees. These methods emphasize that it is possible to attain set goals and in doing so, encourage others to see that with continued effort, they too can also be rewarded as a champion. Methods that amplify individual and group successes include:

- **Group/Team recognition.** For example, if a walking group or a departmental team have walked 1,000,000 steps, publicize this achievement with photographs of the team and even a video.
- **Celebrations.** Reward achievers by throwing a small party and giving out awards.
- **Leadership.** Give recognition both publicly and in annual evaluations for individuals who take the lead with wellness initiatives.

- **Widen your reach** by offering communications that include family members.
- **Share the positive statistics.** People love to be a part of something that is going well. Show the numbers of employees who are attending different programs and why this is positive.
- **Include a variety of mediums** to allow for different languages spoken and access to a computer at work or at home.

**Technology**

The innovations in technology and their applications in the wellness arena are evolving each year and your organization should consider the ones whose functions best meet your specific needs and demographics. The applications can help employees manage a variety of health concerns as well as provide information and analytics to assist with tracking behavior changes. In particular, the information can also be utilized when you conduct your evaluation phase, which is explained in the following chapter.

**Review Checklist**
1. Determine the additional resources you need to support programs
2. Use an evidence-based approach to create fun and relevant interventions to motivate employees to participate in the wellness program
3. Develop new programs to educate employees
4. Put together a comprehensive plan and team for the health fair
5. Develop a health fair program to cover awareness, screenings, and demonstrations

6. Create an effective recognition program in your organization
7. Reward individuals and teams using a variety of methods

# CHAPTER 7

## Step Seven: Evaluation

*"This Is The Way We Do Things Around Here!"*

Evaluation and research are key requisites of every program and are an ongoing process throughout the life of each activity from its conception to completion. There is no one-size-fits-all approach to designing a wellness program and this will be reflected in your evaluation methods as you tailor them to suit the programs that you have put in place, along with your knowledge of the corporate culture and the requirements of the stakeholders and executives. Much is expected of the wellness team by executives regarding the wellness programs: from proving that a program is bringing positive health results, to justifying costs and showing that programs are fiscally prudent. Using the appropriate measuring tools will assist you in determining how a program is performing and if it is aligned with the wellness vision.

When a culture of wellness is achieved, the general consensus will be *"This is the way we do things around here!"*

Evaluations are varied and can be complex in their calculations. So much so that the information on how to conduct an evaluation could fill a book on its own! Useful resources are available from the Health Enhancement Research Organization and from the Population Health Alliance. Links are available in the Appendix section.

In this chapter, I have chosen to provide a selection of the key assessments that you may want to consider using, especially if your organization is small to mid-sized (less than 1,000 employees), along with brief explanations to assist you in making a decision as to which ones you may wish to incorporate into your planning, as well as the types of data to assess. Evaluation takes many forms and can incorporate both formal actions and more relaxed and casual observations:

- Surveys
- Break-even analysis
- Interim assessments
- Informal discussions
- Measuring risk factors
- Observing any positive behavior changes
- Assessing claims data
- Determining Value On Investment
- Wellness program feedback
- HRA's

However in order to evaluate any aspect of a program the item that is to be evaluated must be tangible. In other words, it has to be something that can actually be examined and produce quantifiable results. While evaluations are not constant and rolling along at every step of the program, information should be gathered at regular points depending on the type of programming that is to be assessed. This means that the team will need to be clear on what will be evaluated, when it will occur, who will perform the evaluations, and what will be done with the information that is acquired.

**The Purpose Of An Evaluation**

This can be broken down into three main components:

1. To determine your level of success with each program and garner interest by new participants.
2. To share the information in a measurable way with management and other stakeholders.
3. To secure funding for future programs.

Program evaluation can take place at the end of a one-time intervention and also during and following a long-term program that may be in place for several years, however, both evaluations require a precise approach with a clear structure in place. The CDC describes program evaluation for public health as the *"examination of the worth, merit, or significance of an object."* This is a broad description for use in multiple disciplines where program evaluation needs to take place, in this case, corporate wellness programs, and while a variety of aspects of a program can be evaluated it is essential that a clear and thorough evaluation plan be developed with definitive targets, objectives, processes and analysis of the results put in place.

Thinking about your own organization, decide what purpose the evaluation will provide:

- How will it help the organization achieve its needs?

- How will it improve the wellbeing of your employees and effect positive change-behavior?
- What specific aspects of the program do you want to evaluate?
- What benchmarks will determine if a program is successful?
- What does executive management find credible and of value?
- Did the program meet its objectives?

Evaluation will also provide you with insight into a program's successes as well as areas that require improvement or even cancelation.

### General Overview of Evaluations

As mentioned, an evaluation typically occurs following each intervention or activity, allowing the wellness team to make program adjustments as necessary, as well as helping them to manage and present a better service at the next wellness initiative based on employee feedback, statistics of costs, and participation. There are some evaluations that can be used prior to the launch of an intervention, helping the wellness team determine if a program is likely to be cost-effective or assess the known risk factors. In addition, you should also plan on an annual post-project review to examine the responses of employees, their connection to the program, motivation levels, as well as be able to deliver information on concrete comparisons such as percentage reduction in weight loss or smoking, and the number of days off work due to illness. The details of the wellness plan, the efficacy of the interventions and their performance should be evaluated for quality, engagement, and the resources used.

A combination of participation and resource statistics is useful as are questionnaires that rate meaningfulness and enjoyment. Follow-up and review are critical in measuring the effectiveness of interventions on change behavior and their relevance to attaining both personal and corporate goals. Also, gathering suggestions and feedback from employees who took part will quickly help you to learn from each event as they share their experiences, self-awareness around challenges and strengths, and any positive shifts in lifestyle behavior.

Evaluation data should be gathered after each intervention, several months later to evaluate it against behavior change, and annually against program goals, vision, and Value On Investment (VOI) and Return On Investment (ROI). Data is ongoing and the results of some interventions may not be determined until three to five years after its launch. Follow-up and review is critical in measuring their effectiveness on change behavior and their relevance to attaining both personal and corporate goals.

### The Evaluation Plan

Planning for the evaluation should take place in advance of the initiation of the intervention in order to tie in the various factors that need to be assessed and determine when, what, and how the evaluation should take place. It is very hard to initiate an evaluation without the proper preparation and a clear plan in place before the program begins. It is best practice to be diligent about identifying who is involved in each step of the program, documenting the costs involved, and evaluating and analyzing the results of the established programs.

There are three main areas that evaluations will focus on:

- Financial
- Organizational
- Employee

For each program that you are going to implement, create a baseline of known data such as demographics, information from needs-based surveys, HRA's, and similar data points. These will help you to know how successful a program has been based on this initial information. Performing an evaluation, therefore, allows you to assess the distinctive tangible aspects that demonstrate the program's strengths as well as heightening specific areas to focus on, or even programs to drop.

Further, the amalgamation of assessments, surveys and cultural data that has been carefully gathered, evaluated, and analyzed must then be filed in a secure and accessible environment.

### Process, Impact, and Outcome Metrics

When planning for an evaluation, there are also three additional aspects that are useful to apply in order to assist you in analyzing and interpreting all aspects of the data that you acquire. These are:

- Process
- Impact
- Outcome

Each of these will help you to determine what to evaluate, how to categorize the program elements, and their relationship with resources, ROI, and VOI. Knowing what to evaluate will also depend on the program model that you have chosen to implement, i.e. fun-driven, activity-oriented, or results-driven. Your evaluations can be multi-fold and also have a strategical or tactical focus and purpose. Each metric should be applied to a specific program to gauge the effectiveness of the features and elements that have been built into the program, and ultimately measure the type of influence that they have had. The results will allow you to evaluate a program based on the criteria established when formulating the wellness plan.

## Process Metrics

Evaluating the process of your program allows you to assess the various steps and actions that you and the wellness team took in order to both plan and implement an event. By examining each part of the process, you can determine which areas were successful and moved the project forward, which areas were costly or poorly implemented, and even which ones were unnecessary. This applies to not only every step of the strategic program plan but also to production costs, communication methods, participation and engagement, and educational or training products.

**Typical Process metrics can include the following areas:**
- VOI
- Injuries
- Program participation
- Breakdown of costs of a program
- Data from HRA's
- Pre-paid gym membership usage
- Surveys related to policy changes and how they are received
- Focus groups related to the overall perception of the wellness program
- Productivity surveys

- Break-even analysis prior to initiating a program

As you can see by the wide range of potential metrics to analyze and evaluate, deciding what to measure is dependent upon the goals and objectives of your program, what results are important to executive management, and whether the current programs that you have put in place have demonstrated the desired behavior change.

**Impact Metrics**

The impact of an intervention or program is typically assessed to measure its effect soon after completion and to determine the effectiveness of the program against the short and long-term objectives. It can also be used to determine the "what-if" scenario by evaluating if any changes were a direct result of the program or whether the changes would have happened regardless.

**Typical Impact metrics can include the following areas:**
- Changes in pre and post program habits
- Employees overall experience of programs
- Changes in health risk indicators, e.g. tobacco use reduction
- Impact of educational programs
- Turnover and recruitment changes
- Effectiveness of communication materials
- Ability to implement a new skill

This type of evaluation focuses on the effects of a particular course of action within a program. Additionally, you can explore what type of impression it has made on participants, what discernable benefits have been produced, and if you can even tell, albeit subjectively, by observing body language if people are enjoying a program.

## Outcome Metrics

Evaluating the outcome of a program comes with a degree of flexibility in that the outcome can be measured at different intervals throughout the life of the program, be applied to events that last one day, right through to ones that are in existence over a period of years. A longer time-period is more common when conducting an outcome evaluation as the programs themselves typically require months, if not years, of implementation before goals are achieved, however, earlier results may show a trend in the desired direction. Monitoring an area of outcome over a designated period and at set intervals helps to illuminate early on if there is a need to apply additional steps if a program appears to be floundering or if participation levels are dropping. Further, it allows you to take the necessary action to put the program back on track, an action that would not be possible if a regular evaluation of the Process, the Impact, or the Outcome did not take place.

**Typical Outcome subjects can include the following areas:**
- ROI
- A reduction or increase in medical costs
- Nutritional programs
- Physical programs
- Results of smoking cessation programs
- Absenteeism
- Illnesses
- Lost workdays

- Disability
- Savings related to health-care costs

**Timeframe**

When you were structuring your initial plan for the wellness program, you analyzed employee demographics, carried out surveys, and acquired as much information as was necessary to help you select the best types of interventions for employees while factoring in costs and the length of time that a program would run. Likewise, when deciding **when** to evaluate what you have put in place, you should consider multiple characteristics of your programs to determine the types of assessments you will perform, and when you will conduct them.

A realistic timeframe is important otherwise a program will either be evaluated too early or too late. If it is conducted too early, there may be insufficient data, or the poor results may indicate that a program is not working when it has simply not had sufficient time to develop into a positive outcome. Also, different programs require different times to mature in order to be assessed, for example, a lunch and learn session can be evaluated immediately following the event with five or so questions on paper or using an e-questionnaire such as Survey Monkey; a daily walking program might be evaluated after eight weeks; while a tobacco cessation program may need to be assessed after a minimum of six months. Likewise, a claims analysis may require an even longer period, up to two years, between evaluations, due to the length of time that it can take in order to show the impact of the overall program.

A periodic evaluation of your programs helps you to stay on-track by "checking in" on what's working and what needs further review. Do bear in mind that some programs require many months or years before they show a positive outcome, however by checking in on a regular basis you can identify, for example, what has low participation or is exceeding costs, and adjust accordingly.

Therefore, the timing of when to evaluate a program can depend on a number of factors, including the reality that some will demonstrate benefits earlier, while others will take significantly longer to show lasting positive change to habits that have most likely been established over many years.

## Who Will Perform The Evaluation?

Worksite wellness evaluation requires particular skills and training to ensure that each evaluation is consistent and, if your organization is large enough, to appoint an evaluation team to decide what questions your organization wants or needs to evaluate and to manage the entire evaluation process. Additionally, your organization may also choose to hire a third party to conduct the evaluation. Typically, you will want to appoint an employee who is either certified in wellness evaluation or has program/project management certification to manage the evaluations, analyze the data, and generate reports on it. Assigning responsibility ensures that regular evaluation and reporting will take place and be measured against the pre-set goals, in order to ensure that the program is on track and that the goals remain viable.

## Defining And Capturing Program Data

"Is it working?" This is beyond doubt the one question that will be asked of any of the interventions of a wellness program. It is great to be able to answer confidently that Yes! it is working, however, how will you know? When will you know? What needs to be put in place in order for a thorough evaluation to take place?

For your first evaluation, the documents that you create will form the baseline to be used in this and future evaluations. Looking forward, you will introduce new policies and amend existing ones as the program matures. Data tracking occurs pre and post an intervention, with the post data arriving after or even during the event itself. When interventions have concluded, there will also be a series of pre-defined measures and actions that the designated evaluation person will want to conduct and evaluate, such as:

- Obtaining feedback from participants
- Percentage of participation
- Financial data (money spent or saved)
- Resources used
- Executive leadership involvement
- Satisfaction with the program content and any guest speakers
- How the intervention measured up against the pre-determined goals
- Any positive changes in health behavior
- Any follow-up reports and actions that need to be implemented

On a practical level, the information that evaluations provide is immensely valuable, enabling you to look along the timeline of your programs. For example, new policies that have been put in place will be evaluated to see if they have been effective. Later, there will be a need to determine the quantifiable values related to policies such as, what are the costs and resources associated with implementing the policy? How does it relate to the outcome and efficacy of an intervention?

173

Like any successful project, appropriate attention in the early decision-making stages will serve to establish guideposts, which in this case refers to the general prerequisites for evaluation. Documentation will occur throughout the life of any project, and a wellness program will require detailed, timely, and accessible records of costs, resources, assessments, policies, the percentage of the population at high-risk, participation results, and what is acceptable participation.

Every document should be filed in an accessible place due to the amount of time that can pass between researching, designing, implementing, and evaluating a program. This is especially relevant when evaluations take place many months after the initiation of a program or multiple people are involved. A consistent set of metrics needs to be in place to allow analysis over time, especially when memories have faded and employees may even have left the company. Also, from an auditing perspective, it is best practice to have all information documented and available.

## Evaluation Tools

Having determined what you will evaluate, and when, we will now take a look at some of the tools at your disposal that can be used to acquire the information and how they will help you measure and assess the interventions, policies, and claims. The following evaluation methods are by no means exhaustive and there may others that you wish to choose that are not listed here. Evaluation tools include:

- Surveys
- Post program questionnaires
- Absenteeism reports
- Presenteeism reports

- HRA's
- Annual screening reports
- Productivity reports
- Informal and interim evaluations
- Break-even analysis
- Budget versus actual costs
- Risk factor assessments
- Claims data analysis reports
- Value On Investment reports
- Wellness program progress reports
- Exit interviews

There is no right or wrong method to choose; it is simply a matter of reviewing your goals, determining which part of the Process, the Impact, or the Outcome you wish to evaluate, and then selecting one or more tools that will help you capture or measure the information that you require. For example, if the focus of the tobacco cessation wellness program is to reduce the number of people who use tobacco products by 20 percent through a group coaching intervention, you may want to track the number of participants, the cost of a coach, and the number of participants who stop using these products after six and 12 months and comparing how these results compare with the original goals that were set for the program and the intervention. You may also want to consider how the role of this intervention and program has impacted, if any, employee satisfaction by comparing current surveys with the surveys that were performed at the inception of the program.

The wellness team, or the designated evaluation person, should also work on clarifying the types of questions that an evaluation will need to answer. The tools can be used to analyze a variety of programs, demographics, and to gather statistics including:

- Gauge the percentage of participants
- Changes in behavior
- The effectiveness of interventions
- The relevance of interventions
- If the day and time was convenient
- Overall satisfaction with the interventions
- The speakers' effectiveness and knowledge
- Any effects on company culture and teams
- What is the impact on policies that were created or changed?
- Costs involved and any accrued savings since the implementation of the intervention and wellness program
- If people are they utilizing and sharing what they have learned
- If the intervention was deemed to be useful
- If the program met the goals and objectives
- What is the feedback from champions?

**Conducting An Evaluation**

Gauging the success of a program is made easier by laying a solid framework to weave the threads of the evaluation process through. Program participants, in particular, will have opinions on what they thought of the content of a program, how engaging a guest speaker was, how informative or relevant the educational material was, and a whole host of other thoughts related to the programs offered. Their views and sentiments matter and it is up to the wellness team to determine what will be evaluated, how it will be researched, who and how it will be communicated to, and what changes to existing and future programming will be done as a result of the analyzing the information. Thorough preparation will ensure that the wellness team is clear on what they are evaluating and to whom they will share the results.

Regardless if this is the first time an evaluation has been performed on a particular program or to update existing information, the person or team involved in carrying out the evaluation needs to establish as many details about the program as possible. This includes:

- Full knowledge of the scope of the program
- Acquiring the names of the individual or team involved in organizing the program
- The date the program started and the length of time it has been running
- The aims of the program
- What prior evaluations, if any, have been done against the program?
- Reviewing the metrics of the evaluation that were defined at the planning stage prior to implementation
- The format for reporting the evaluation findings

While we are always hoping for a positive outcome and a program that is achieving its desired goals, this is not always the case. Programs can fail for multiple reasons and it is not necessarily a reflection on the program manager or the wellness team. Ultimately, the data indicates the results and the accumulated information can be a great help in answering questions as to why a program is not doing delivering the expected results, or helping you to determine what aspects have outlived their usefulness and need to be updated or retired, or what qualities and properties you should enhance. Try not to be despondent if the results are not what you are expecting. Keep an open mind and embrace the information.

## Measuring Value On Investment (VOI)

The holistic approach to wellness is a shift from solely looking at the bottom line and other healthcare drivers to embracing a broad and more complete attitude towards wellness and what it means to be healthy. VOI is frequently seen as a Human Capital Investment (HCI) and companies who purposefully invest in HCI are the ones who see the highest returns on their bottom line through stronger worker performance, increased productivity, and support for programs. There are thousands of companies worldwide who invest a considerable amount of their budget towards their employees including: Goldman Sachs, HP, Oracle, and ConAgra Foods. However, companies of **any** size, who recognize the importance of the connection of their employees to their business and the need to invest in training, recruitment and retention, and also wellness programs, can and **should** invest in HCI.

VOI can be measured through the identifiable improvements, level of engagement, and level of satisfaction, all of which require continuous effort in order to uphold the goals and mission of the wellness program and nurture an ongoing culture of health. It takes a considerable amount of time to integrate these intrinsic values into the wellness programs in order to allow them to express their full significance and worth. The multifaceted aspects of VOI do not happen overnight; they take time to be processed, experienced, and developed.

VOI analysis is a tool that is tailored to your organization as every company's culture and business goals are different. Thinking about your own organization, you will want to consider how you will use this stratagem to measure areas such as:

- Productivity
- Engagement
- Absenteeism
- Presenteeism
- Job satisfaction

One or more of these aspects can be linked to a specific wellness program in order to gauge the program's overall success. It's worth noting that rising health care costs in the U.S. were predicted to reach 19 percent of America's gross domestic product by 2015. While not traditionally associated with direct financial returns, VOI does affect the bottom line through indirect methods. Some methods you may wish to use include:

- Primary drivers. How are programs and employees measuring up against the wellness goals?
- Secondary drivers. Measuring the rate of employee turnover, job satisfaction, motivation, and participation in programs.
- Analyzing how successful the programs are at minimizing present health risks and preventing employees from developing new illnesses or conditions.
- Analyzing community involvement and reputation.
- Reviewing the number of sick days used, workers compensation, and disability costs.
- Healthcare utilization and hospital visits.
- Compliance with preventive screenings.
- The use of surveys to gauge the culture of health.

- Asking anonymous questions such as "how likely are you to recommend the company to a friend?
- Reviewing productivity, employee turnover, retention, teamwork, and morale.

Be as creative as possible in your methods and approach when measuring VOI. Also, as more peer organizations embrace the intrinsic qualities of investing in employees and adopting a broader approach to wellness, it will become easier to make the case for VOI to executive leadership.

**Measuring Return On Investment (ROI)**

A 2010 study by the Robert Wood Johnson Foundation found that a corporate wellness plan, on average, contributed to a "25 percent reduction in associated health plan and disability costs. ROI can be used to justify the introduction of a program or help in the decision to end an existing one. It is basically a means of determining the cost to implement a program against the actual savings. Unlike the previous measurement tools, the ROI is not something that can be performed immediately following a program as it is typically looking at expected costs, actual costs and expected savings and actual savings. There is also the added factor whereby predicted savings can change due to better or worsening health outcomes, catastrophic health claims, and the length of time and costs involved in analyzing data on a monthly and annual basis.

Sadly, there are times when a catastrophic health issue happens to one or more employees and should not be seen as a sign that the wellness program is not effective. It will be included in the data, however there will be multiple parameters that you will analyze over the course of the first year of the program to determine the success of aspects of the program, and while this may show a spike in one area of the data, overall the data can show if the general trend is positive, even with the catastrophic health issue. The financial and non-economic differentials that you may want to consider measuring include:

- HRA's
- In-house program costs
- Complexity and length of programs
- Financial costs and salaries of in-house personnel such as coaches, trainers, evaluators, and wellness program consultants
- Program communication and participation
- Incentive costs
- Outsourcing screenings
- Emergency room visits
- Behavior changes and maintenance
- Lost productivity due to days off work
- Health claims
- Employee retention and turnover
- Recruitment costs for replacement hires

Consider the needs of your business when you are making the decision as to which aspects you wish to measure. If you are skilled in conducting evaluations or are outsourcing this area to a specialist, you may also want to consider looking at outside factors which may have positively or negatively affected the outcome of your results. In other words, would the outcome have happened anyway, regardless of whether or not the wellness program was in place?

## Break-Even Analysis

A break-even analysis is normally used to help a company determine how many units of their product they need to sell at a fixed price in order to cover the fixed costs that they incur to produce the product. With a wellness program, there is often no obvious product, however a break-even analysis is particularly useful when calculating scenarios such as whether to use health coaches, implement smoking cessation programs, assess the cost of or whether to build an onsite fitness center with equipment and trained staff, or outsource the fitness center program to a nearby gym and offer discounts to employees. Basically, you are determining if all the known benefits of your wellness program will offset the actual costs that have been, or will be, incurred during set-up and actually running the program.

As was mentioned at the start of this chapter, the aspect of a wellness program that is to be evaluated must be tangible. In other words it has to be something that can be measured and quantified. Your application of S.M.A.R.T. goals also applies to evaluations in that the assessment has to be conducted in a realistic timeframe, having allowed the program to develop and evolve, in order to have sufficient data parameters to assess.

In the early stages, the data that is gathered can be itemized on a monthly basis, eventually becoming quarterly, as more information on costs and participation rates are known. The key is to use a systematic approach, document the data that you obtain at each stage, use graphs, spreadsheets, and dashboards to present the information to executive management, integrate a realistic timeline, and be consistent in managing the ongoing analysis and interpretation of the data.

A break-even analysis is a view into the future and gives you a great deal of control. You can apply it to a variety of programs, both new or existing, to better guide you in strategizing current and future aspects of programming. Most interventions will have up-front costs and may take weeks, months, even years before benefits are seen that outweighs costs and it is worth being conscious of the need to do this type of analysis months later when an intervention has concluded or meets an annual milestone.

Typically, it is utilized later in the evaluation stage to compare data, determine the benefits of running a particular program and if it is following the agreed track, monitor incentives, and even help establish if the program should be expanded. A break-even analysis is also flexible enough to be used prior to an event to determine if the allocated resources are too much or too little, that goals and benefits have been established, and determine the risk-reduction required in order to break-even.

## Communication

The final part of the evaluation is the communication of your findings. Who needs to have the reports? Is it only executive leaders or should aspects be conveyed to employees too? In chapters one and two, thorough planning was emphasized, including the reporting structure to ensure that it complied with your culture and delivered appropriate information in a timely manner.

Obviously, there is no point in gathering and analyzing data and not doing anything with it. If part of your evaluation process involves a survey of program participants, you can be certain that most of the employees who completed the survey will want to know the outcome of the results and what you are going to do with the data that you have now acquired. After all, if an employee has taken the time to complete a survey, (compounded for each participant it's a lot of time) there has to be a clear purpose and benefit to employees, all stakeholders, and the organization. For example:

- Are you gathering information to assess the status of a particular program and seeking to identify areas that require modification?
- Will the data be used to determine the success of a program or the need to drop it?
- Will the information garnered be used for reporting purposes to executive management?
- Do you know what is important to executive management and key stakeholders so that you can present the data that they need to continue funding existing and future wellness programs?
- Do you need to know what participants think about a program and if you need to reassess your objectives to either improve it or drop it?
- Are you gathering data to promote employee successes?

Communicating the appropriate information to stakeholders should be done in a manner that is conducive to how they like to receive reports. Executive leadership will require a thorough update of the findings, to help them to justify the outlay of resources and see a return on the value of their investment. Find out as early as possible if they only want to read an executive summary or if detailed reports and a formal presentation. Distilling the information requires you to know what aspects of the programs will reveal the most pertinent facts relevant to executive leadership, in order to show

how the culture of wellness is creating a positive shift, not only on health, but on productivity, job satisfaction, and morale too. Expressing the information clearly and succinctly with diagrams, statistics, and itemizing participants' feedback is frequently better received than writing up a 30-page report. In addition, you will need to establish how a company-wide communication is to be distributed so that you can engage everyone in the evolving results and program success. And you will also want to consider how to handle questions and feedback as a result of a company-wide communication. There are bound to be a few!

However, just as the wellness team was creative in their program offerings, communicating the findings of the evaluations to employees is also an area where the team can be creative in maintaining a positive buzz around programs. Rather than giving out all the information in one swoop, consider using the information as part of your marketing plan. A medical device company placed a poster in the cafeteria showing that since implementing healthier snack option there was a 45 percent reduction in soda purchases, a computer software company placed a poster in an elevator and by the stairs to highlight that the "Let's Move" campaign resulted in 81 percent of employees signing up and walking a total of 1000 miles, and an aerospace company placed a photograph (with approvals from the individuals represented) in the break room depicting the employees who successfully quit smoking following participation in a tobacco cessation program.

Break the information down into bite-sized chunks that can be savored and absorbed.

## Conclusion

The pursuit of wellness, in all its variations, can be a diverse journey that is at times demanding, at other times effortless and not something to think about, and yet we know that ultimately good health is a rewarding and very necessary destination. It's often not until there is a health scare with either ourselves, or someone close to us, that we pay attention and realize that we have to get serious about health. Wellness encompasses all aspects of our life, whether we are at work, at home, or in the community.

Equipped with this book and the additional resources mentioned in the appendix, you will now have the resources to not only build a wellness program that meets the needs of your organization and your colleagues, but a platform that also raises awareness about approaches towards health, including your own and that of others, and to assist you in becoming a wellness trailblazer. Your creativity around the types of programs offered, the strategies to inspire and engage, and your willingness to be an agent of change will contribute to employees becoming more accountable and willing to participate in taking steps to improve their own health. Creating a wellness program is an amazing opportunity to transform the old mindset and embrace new healthier practices that, with the right environment, will grow and develop into lifelong habits.

It's a great feeling when a culture of wellness is achieved and when you and your colleagues can say "This Is The Way We Do Things Around Here!"

**Review Checklist**

1. Have a clear and thorough evaluation plan in place with definitive targets, objectives, processes and analysis of the results. Ensure they approved by executive management
2. Decide the types of program activities or interventions that you are going to evaluate
3. Define the program evaluation timeline
4. Have measurable results
5. Calculate the ROI to determine if the program cost effective
6. Calculate aspects of the VOI
7. Ascertain if the program goals achieved
8. Determine the most effective aspect of the program
9. Develop and complete a break-even analysis
10. Define a wellness program results communication plan and publish the results
11. Based on the new information, determine if you need to implement new policies
12. Based on the new information, determine what you need to improve

# PART III: Resources

# CHAPTER 8

## 101 Wellness Program Ideas

When considering any wellness program ideas, the wellness team should take into account the variables in demographics, the goals and objectives of the program, and the culture of the company. Multiple approaches are best as they target the different stages of change that individuals are in, address the varied ways that people learn, and offer several opportunities for participation, including overlapping the availability of programs for shift-workers.

There are a variety of tools that the wellness team needs to have in their proverbial toolbox to increase employee participation in wellness, improve productivity and retention, attract top talent, and help the organization be a great place to work. Implementing the programs requires ensuring that the appropriate policies are in place, that program information has been disseminated, and that management are trained and equipped to encourage employees. Additionally, the integration of video, podcasts, and apps with educational materials will improve wellness delivery and help employees to identify their own health conditions, track positive behavior change, and manage their goals.

The following program ideas can be adapted to suit the demographics and culture of your organization and help you to provide programs that are fun, informative, and enable employees to self-manage their health and wellness goals. Additionally, they will transform an existing wellness programs by providing ideas to keep it fresh and enjoyable.

~~~~~~~

## 101 Wellness Program Ideas
### General

1. Create and maintain an intranet web site that includes links to informational nutritional, physical and health resources. Include videos, podcasts and written material.
2. Schedule focus groups to ensure employees have input into what they want to have in their wellness program, their work environment and schedule, and their social setting at work.
3. Hold a Wellness Month event and have a "Tip Of The Week" that is posted at stairwells, cafeteria, lounge areas, and on the intranet.
4. Provide training to enable employees to self-manage minor health conditions e.g. to reduce non-essential trips to E.R. when an appointment could be made at a clinic or advice sought from a pharmacist at a pharmacy.
5. Hold blood drives.

6. Organize community volunteering.
7. Offer group and telephone coaching services.
8. Invite professionals to give educational programs during lunch e.g. nutritional information, exercise demonstrations, stress-management, sleep and fatigue assessments and tips.
9. Hold an educational session that teaches the signs of a stroke and what to do in an emergency situation.
10. Install Automatic External Defibrillators (AED's) and first-aid kits.
11. Have a certified instructor teach CPR classes with 2-year follow-ups.
12. Have a certified instructor teach first aid with 2-year follow-ups.
13. Provide employees with training in AED's plus a refresher course every 2 years.
14. Provide employees with Epi-Pen training.
15. Provide a lactation/feeding room (and policies in place to permit time to spend in room).
16. Place a wellness bulletin board in a high-traffic area.
17. Have a reading area of informative and educational books, pamphlets, DVD's from both local and national sources that employees can borrow.
18. Tie in educational wellness days with the National Health Observances calendar.
19. Offer annual screenings for cholesterol, breast, and prostate.
20. Have a wall of achievement.

21. Recognize achievements with certificates, trophies, and an email or printed letter from the senior executive of your organization.
22. Offer flu shots for employees and families.
23. Offer financial wellness program to show employees how they can buy new fitness equipment, apparel, or fund a vacation.
24. Promote a green environment by enforcing a vehicle anti-idling policy.
25. Use Environmentally Preferable Products (EPP).
26. Offer rewards on a sliding scale, e.g. give an award 2-3 months after an employee has reached their target weight goal. This is to encourage maintenance of the goal.
27. Take a professional, financial, cultural, or similar topic and use it in one of the major program models to promote a focused area of subject matter.
28. Never launch a program during open enrollment but DO start discussions about the new program and that it will start on e.g. Jan 1st.
29. Post information on the success of programs on break-room walls.
30. Add a calendar of wellness events on inside of bathroom doors.
31. Save on printing out information in different languages by using a pictorial of Do's and Don'ts.
32. Create a policy of no-smoking in company vehicles.
33. Use tele-medicine to encourage preventative screening and for employees to have easy access to their health data such as cholesterol, blood pressure, and blood sugar levels.

34. Hold men's health issues information sessions on issues such as prostate screening, testicular self-exam, cardiovascular disease, and stress management.

35. Hold women's health issues information sessions on issues such as breast self-exam, ovarian cancer education, pap screening, cardiovascular disease, and stress management.

36. Provide the latest nutritional, physical, and emotional advice that is shown to slow the aging process.

37. Decide upfront which incentives and rewards will be used in the program.

38. If requested by employees who share a common health issue, enable them to organize their own support group.

39. Provide information for women on planning to become pregnant.

40. Volunteer as a company at least twice a year in local non-profit organizations such as animal rescue or food pantry.

## Physical

41. During long meetings, invite attendees to move around and stretch for a few minutes each hour.

42. Sponsor team fitness challenges within the organization.

43. Increase fitness goals every quarter.

44. Go somewhere! Have a destination rather than simply aiming to walk 10,000 steps. For example, if your company is based in eastern Massachusetts, turn the number of steps walked into a competition and plan e.g. a "Walk to Cape Cod" competition with points awarded

along the trail for achievements reached. The winner and a partner receive a weekend at a B&B in a town in Cape Cod.

45. Hold a bi-annual fitness equipment swap.
46. Secure subsidized membership at fitness centers.
47. Health Insurance companies will provide an annual monetary incentive for attendance/membership at a fitness class, yoga class, or gym.
48. Use gaming technology. Have a Wii Boxing tournament or a Wii Olympics and give out medals to the winners.
49. Use apps such as a Hot Seat App to encourage employees to move regularly.
50. Have foosball tables or other fun activities available.
51. Promote the use of stairs rather than an elevator.
52. Launch a daily walking club at lunchtime.
53. Provide a home safety checklist to avoid injuries at home.
54. Offer sun prevention and skin cancer education.
55. Hold skin cancer checks by a practitioner trained in recognizing different moles and skin cancer.
56. Hold an informal sports league of whatever sport or sports are popular amongst the employees to encourage more movement.
57. Arrange for an ergonomic specialist to do a presentation and demonstration on upright desk options.
58. Teach proper lifting techniques in a "Safe to Work" program in order to prevent injury.

59. Install outdoor fitness and sports equipment.
60. Offer on-site fitness programs.
61. Provide accessible showers and changing areas.
62. Provide secure on-site bicycle storage and/or racks.
63. Hold a bike inspection and helmet-fitting day with a trained fitter from a local independent bike store.
64. Encourage sponsored activities and provide corporate sponsorship match of amount raised or to a set limit.
65. Schedule weekly yoga classes.
66. Invite a demonstration of martial arts.
67. Truck Stop and Parking Tips. Park further away in order to stretch and walk more.
68. Have a physical trainer teach tips on staying fit at a desk
69. Invite a chiropractor to teach good posture while sitting at a desk or in a vehicle.
70. Schedule groups to take a course with a qualified instructor at your state's defensive driving course.

## Stress Reduction

71. Provide a quiet space that can be used for stress management/reduction including prayer and meditation.
72. Have "Fido Fridays" in small offices with dog-loving employees and well-trained dogs.
73. Create an area with rockers and comfortable armchairs.
74. Hold meetings outdoors.

75. Have lunch and learn events and experiential sessions to educate participants on healthy responses to stress.
76. Ensure employees take lunch breaks.
77. Offer monthly chair massage sessions.
78. Schedule daily chair massages at end-of-quarter or when major projects are due.
79. Have meditation sessions.
80. Schedule relaxation workshops.
81. Hold educational sessions on resiliency and strategies to deal with demands at work and home.
82. Hold domestic violence awareness seminars
83. Invite a financial wellness speaker.
84. Invite dependent care specialists to discuss available options for employees who are caring for a senior relative.
85. Schedule monthly work-life balance sessions.
86. Invite an expert in sleep management to talk about fatigue, sleep disorders, and how to improve sleep.
87. Bring in plants and make either an indoor or outdoor green area.
88. Schedule a regular (weekly, bi-weekly, or monthly) cartoon show or funny movie.
89. Encourage use of private music (using head phones).

## Nutritional

90. Arrange for local organic vendors to take and deliver orders for fresh produce and breads.
91. Hold a "Biggest Loser" competition.

92. Have a "five-a-day" challenge to encourage eating a minimum of 5 fruits and vegetables daily.
93. Provide easily identifiable labeling of healthier vending machine food and drink options.
94. Arrange for monthly lunch-n-learn sessions by local nutritionists and informative sessions on pre-diabetes management and reversal.
95. Hold a monthly healthy cooking class (day or evening).
96. On St Patrick's day/week, have an "Eat Your Greens" promotion.
97. Have a "Project Zero" competition around holiday time with the purpose of not gaining any weight.
98. Have a Happy Healthy Hour e.g. 5pm-6pm at an organic food store or a Lunch and Learn Happy Healthy Hour.
99. Provide weekly food samples.
100.Create a list of healthy options in fast-food restaurants.
101. Have a formal weight loss group to provide monitor weight-loss, nutritional advice, and support.

# Appendix

## General Resources: Guide To Internet Resources, Agencies, And Organizations

The following sites provide updated information on their area of expertise and free resources for brochures, posters, and signs. Topics and resources available include:
- Blood pressure Information
- Cholesterol Information
- Clinical Preventive Services
- Diabetes information
- Education Programs
- Evaluation of Programs
- Heart Disease and Stroke Prevention
- Implementation Strategies for Screening and Control (CDC)
- Risk Assessment Tools
- Tobacco Cessation, Self-Directed Quitting Tools
- Toolkits
- Tools and Resources (videos, quizzes, materials) (AHA)
- Return On Investment (ROI) Calculator
- Worksite Stairwell Interventions

Alcohol Treatment ROI Calculator:
www.alcoholcostcalculator.org/roi

American Academy of Sleep Medicine:
www.sleepeducation.com

American Cancer Society: www.cancer.org

American College of Sports Medicine: www.acsm.org

American Diabetes Association: www.diabetes.org

American Heart Association (AHA): www.heart.org

American Lung Association: www.lungusa.org

American Red Cross: www.redcross.org

Centers for Disease Control and Prevention (CDC):
www.cdc.gov

CDC Guide to Breastfeeding Interventions:
www.cdc.gov/breastfeeding

Dads Against Drunk Driving: www.DADD.org

Diabetes at Work: www.diabetesatwork.org

Dietary Guidelines of America:
www.health.gov/dietaryguidelines/

Disease Prevention: www.Healthypeople.gov

Employers Against Domestic Violence:
www.employersagainstdomesticviolence.org

Food and Drug Administration: www.fda.gov

Green Streets Initiative (Massachusetts):
www.gogreenstreets.org

Guide to Community Preventive Services:
www.thecommunityguide.org

Harvard Medical School Division of Sleep Medicine Sleep
and Health Education Program:
www.understandingsleep.org

Health Enhancement Research Organization (HERO).
www.hero-health.org

Kaiser Family Foundation State Health Facts:
www.statehealthfacts.org

Local Harvest: Farmers markets: www.localharvest.org

March of Dimes: www.marchofdimes.com

Massachusetts Health Promotion Clearinghouse: provides
free pamphlets and information:
www.maclearinghouse.com

Mothers Against Drunk Driving: www.madd.org

National Business Group on Health:
www.businessgrouphealth.org

National Diabetes Information Clearinghouse:
www.diabetes.niddk.nih.gov/dm/pubs/preventionprogra
m

National Diabetes Program, National Institutes of Health:
www.ndep.nih.gov/resources/business.html

National Health Observances:
www.healthfinder.gov/nho/default.aspx

National Heart, Lung, and Blood Institute:
www.nhlbi.nih.gov/health/public/heart/hbp/hbpwallet.ht
ml

National Sleep Foundation: www.sleepfoundation.org

National Wellness Institute www.nationalwellness.org

Partnership for Prevention: www.prevent.org

Partnership for Workplace Mental Health:
www.workplacementalhealth.org

Population Health Alliance. Information on program
evaluations. www.PopulationHealthAlliance.org

Tobacco Cessation Resources:

> www.makesmokinghistory.org

> www.smokefree.gov

> www.TrytoStop.org

> www.quitworks.org

United States Breastfeeding Committee:
www.usbreastfeeding.org

U S Department of Agriculture Food Pyramid:
www.mypyramid.gov

US Department of Health and Human Services Dietary Guidelines for Americans
www.health.gov/DietaryGuidelines

Wellness Council of America: www.welcoa.org

Worksite Wellness Council of Massachusetts:
www.wwcma.org

# Bibliography

## Chapter 1

Nyce, Steven. (2012, November). Association Between Changes in Health Risk Status and Changes in Future Health Care Costs: A Multiemployer Study. *Journal of Occupational and Environmental Medicine, 54(11): 1364 – 1373.*

Baicker, K., Cutler, D., Song, Z. (2010). *Workplace Wellness Programs can Generate Savings.* Health Affairs.

The Harvard Business Review HBR. (2010). *The pillars of an effective workplace wellness program.*

Doran, G. T. (1981). There's a S.M.A.R.T. way to write management's goals and objectives. *Management Review (AMA FORUM)* 70 (11): 35–36.

Health Enhancement Research Organization, American College of Occupational and Environmental Medicine, American Cancer Society, American Diabetes Society, and American Heart Society. (2012). Guidance for a Reasonably Designed, Employer-Sponsored Wellness Program Using Outcomes-Based Incentives. *JOEM,* Volume 54, Number 7, July 2012

Centers for Disease Control and Prevention. *Steps to Wellness: A guide to Implementing the 2008 Physical Guidelines for Americans in the Workplace.* Atlanta: U.S. Department of Health and Human Serivices; 2012.

# Chapter 2

Ha T. Tu, Ralph C. Mayrell. (2010, July) Employer Wellness Initiatives Grow, but Effectiveness Varies Widely. *NIHCR Research* Brief No. 1.

Goodstein, L. D., Nolan, T. M., & Pfeiffer, J. W. (1993). *Applied strategic planning: a comprehensive guide.* New York: McGraw Hill.

Mills, PR., Kessler R.C., Cooper, J., Sullivan, S. Impact of a health promotion program on employee health risks and work productivity. *American Journal of Health Promotion.* (2007 Sep-Oct;22(1): 45-53.

The Kaiser Family Foundation. (2015). Employer Health Benefits. Annual Survey.

Claxton, G., Rae, M., Panchal, N., Whimore, H., Damico, A., Kenward, K., Long, M. *Health Benefits In 2015: Stable Trends In The Employer Market.* Health Affairs.

The Business Case for Wellbeing:
http://www.gallup.com/businessjournal/139373/business-case-wellbeing.aspx

# Chapter 3

Project Management Institute. (2000) *A Guide to the Project Management Body of Knowledge.* (v1.2.).

Baun, W.B., & Pronk, N.P. (2006) Good programs don't just happen-they're planned! *ACSM Health & Fitness Journal,* 10 (3), 40-43.

Bradford, R. W., Duncan, J. P., & Tarcy, B. (2000). *Simplified Strategic Planning.* Worcester, MA: Chandler House Press.

# Chapter 4

Loeppke R. (2008) The value of health and the power of prevention. *Int J Workplace Health Management,* I:95-108.

Finkelstein, E., Strombotne, K. Popkin, B. THE COSTS OF OBESITY AND IMPLICATIONS FOR POLICYMAKERS. *Agriculture & Applied Economics Association.* JEL Classifications: I10, I18, 3rd Quarter 2010, 25(3).

USDA Center for Nutrition Policy and Promotion. 2015. *Food Guide Pyramid.*

Coping with stress at work. 2013. *APA Center for Organizational Excellence.*

# Chapter 5

U.S. Department of Labor (DOL). (2014, January) *Fact sheet on the Affordable Care Act and Wellness Programs.*

U.S. Department of Labor (DOL). *The HIPAA Nondiscrimination Requirements.*

Conn, Vicki S. et al. Meta-Analysis of Workplace Physical

Activity Interventions.
*American Journal of Preventive Medicine,* Volume 37, Issue 4
, 330–339.

Volpp, K., et al. (2009) A Randomized, Controlled Trial of
Financial Incentives for Smoking Cessation. *New England
Journal of Medicine.* 360:699-709.

Peto R, Lopez AD. Koop CE, Pearson CE, Schwarz MR.
Future worldwide health effects of current smoking
patterns. *Critical Issues in Global Health.* San Francisco:
Jossey-Bass; 2000, 154–161.

Stambor, Z. (2005, January). A research study of 245
female students at a Belgian teacher training college
between the ages of 19 and 20 years. *American
Psychological Society.* Vol 36, No1.

Kenneth Thomas. (2009, November/December). The Four
Intrinsic Rewards That Drive Employee Engagement. *Ivey
Business Journal.*

# Chapter 6

Bandura, A. (1997). *Self-Efficacy: The Exercise of Control.*
W.H. Freeman and Company.

Towers Watson. (2009). *Turbocharging Employee
Engagement.*

# Chapter 7

Centers for Disease Control and Prevention. (2012)

*Introduction to Program Evaluation for Public Health Programs: A Self-Study Guide.*

Burton, W., Chen, C., Li ,X., Schultz, A., Kasiarz, D., Edington, DW. Evaluation of a Comprehensive Employee Wellness Program at an Organization With a Consumer-Directed Health Plan. *Journal of Occupational & Environmental Medicine.* 56(4):347-353, 2014 Apr.

Mukhopadhyay S, Wendel J. (2013) Evaluating an employee wellness program. *Int J Health Care Finance Econ.*

https://www.businessgrouphealth.org National business Group on Health (VOI information).

Encyclopedia of Health Economics. Edited by Anthony J Culyer. Elsivier Press.

Nash, D., Reifsnyder, J., Fabius, R., Pracilio, V. (2011) *Population Health: Creating a Culture of Wellness.* Jones and Bartlett Learning, LLC.

Valente, T. (2002). *Evaluating Health Promotion Programs.* Oxford University Press, 11- 17.

# Additional Material

American Psychological Society. (2005, January). Intrinsic/extrinsic motivation article: a single, direct strategy motivates students best. Vol 36, No. 1, Print version: page 20.

Chenoweth, D. H. (2007). Worksite Health Promotion (Second edition). Champaign, IL: *Human Kinetics.*

Grossmeier, J., Terry, P., Cipriotti, A., Burtaine, J. (2010). Best Practices in Evaluating Worksite Health Promotion Programs. *The Art of Health Promotion,* January/February 2010, 1-10.

Harvard Business Review. (2006, October). Reprint R0610B: Sleep Deficit The Performance Killer- A Conversation with Harvard Medical School Professor Charles A. Czeisler.

Epstein, L., Mardon, S. (2006) Harvard Medical School Guide to a Good Night's Sleep. *Harvard Medical School Guides.*

Health Management Research Center. (2000). The Ultimate 20th Century Cost Benefit Analysis and Report. *The University of Michigan,* p 1-39.

Institute of Medicine/National Academies Press: Sleep Disorders and Sleep Deprivation: An Unmet Public Health Problem.

Visscher TL, Seidell JC. (2001). The Public Health Impact Of Obesity. *Annual Review of Public Health.* 22:355-75.

McKenzie, J. F., Neiger, B. L., & Smeltzer, J. L. (2005). *Planning, Implementing & Evaluating Health Promotion Programs.* San Francisco: Pearson Benjamin Cummings.

# Templates

## 3-YEAR INCENTIVE PLAN EXAMPLE

Decide on the type of incentive program your organization with adopt i.e. participation only, such as regular attendance at an approved fitness center, or one that requires a health modification where employees must meet specific requirements to qualify for an incentive such as nutritional changes, percentage of weight loss, or reaching preset fitness goals.

Other options include assigning participation points that can be reimbursed for incentive rewards.

|        | GOAL | INTERVENTION | INCENTIVE |
|--------|------|--------------|-----------|
| **Year 1** | Introduce HRA. | Complete HRA. New employees to complete HRA. | $100 gift cards to complete HRA. |
|        | Create a healthy environment. Offer on-site health education classes and tips to lower stress. | Show prompt appreciation to employees. Survey to determine short and long term stressors. Provide financial counseling. | Free personal coaching of the employees choice. Offer free weekly onsite yoga/meditation classes. |
|        | Reduce the number of employees who are overweight. | Provide educational resources to establish healthy nutritional habits for employees and their families to lower BMI by 10% (within healthy parameters). Provide weight | Provide food-tracking plan. Provide meal planning with a dietician. |

| | | management support groups. | |
|---|---|---|---|
| | Appraise vending food and beverage machine selections. | Offer healthy vending options and educational lunch and learn sessions to support weight reduction. | Subsidize healthy foods in vending machines. Provide lunch boxes. Free 12-week course with a weight management vendor. |
| | Create physical programs. | Initiate daily lunchtime walking groups. | Fitness center reimbursement. |
| | Reduce number of smokers by 50%. | Offer smoking cessation aids to participants such as patches, education, and support classes. Provide group coaching. Develop and implement tobacco policies. | $50 monthly insurance premium discount to employees who do not use tobacco products. |
| **Year 2** | Complete HRA. | Team competition to encourage completion of HRA. | $125 gift cards for completion of HRA. Bonus for team who finishes first. |
| | Increase health fair participation. | Promotion of health fair via intranet and posters. | Gift cards for attending the health fair. |
| | Create a relaxed environment. Provide weekly lunch and learn | Have a weekly comedy DVD during Friday lunchtime, or share vacation pictures. Time-management | Personalize promotional wellness items such as yoga mat bags, monogramed |

|  |  |  |  |
|---|---|---|---|
|  | programs on lowering stress. | course. Implement stretching sessions and policies to ensure regular breaks | towels, sports clothing, or water bottles. |
|  | Appraise cafeteria meals. Offer nutrition programs. Increase the number of physical programs. | Provide on-site weight-loss programs. Add basketball hoops in an outdoor area. | Offer discounts for external weight-loss programs. Provide pedometers, bicycle mileage trackers, sports equipment. |
|  | Increase smoking cessation attempts. | Provide smoking cessation education and coaching. | $50 monthly insurance premium discount to employees who do not use tobacco products. |
| **Year 3** | Complete HRA. | Promotion of HRA via intranet and posters. | $150 gift cards for completion of HRA. An additional $50 if the employee's department has 85% or greater participation in HRA. |
|  | Achieve 70% participation at health fair. | Use intranet and team participation challenges to highlight the fair. | Gift cards for attending the health fair. |

| | | | |
|---|---|---|---|
| | Lower stress through flexi-time work plan. | Introduce flexi-time. Develop and implement policies to support flexi-time. Sleep management course. | Reduced fees for fitness and yoga classes. |
| | Educate employees on healthy eating and disease prevention. | Have a "zero" competition between Thanksgiving and New Year. The challenge is to not gain any weight during this period. | A "members only" lunch for employees who successfully achieve a physical challenge. |
| | Increase the difficulty of physical challenges. | Day field trips with a physical trainer to hone skills. | Company-paid entry fees to competitions. |
| | Eliminate smoking at workplace. | Provide smoking cessation education and coaching. | Reduced deductible for completely stopping tobacco usage. |

# 3-YEAR INCENTIVE PLAN

| | GOAL | INTERVENTION | INCENTIVE |
|---|---|---|---|
| Year 1 | | | |
| | | | |
| | | | |
| | | | |
| | | | |
| Year 2 | | | |
| | | | |
| | | | |
| | | | |
| | | | |
| Year 3 | | | |
| | | | |
| | | | |
| | | | |
| | | | |

# S.M.A.R.T. INTERVENTIONS EXAMPLE

| GOAL<br>With W's | OBJECTIVE<br>With W's | INTERVENTION<br>With W's |
|---|---|---|
| To be a tobacco free workplace. | Reduce the number of smokers by 20% within 12 months. | Offer smoking cessation aids to participants such as patches, education, and support classes.<br>Group coaching.<br>Develop and implement tobacco policies. |
| Promote a healthy environment and support employees. Reduce the number of employees who are overweight to 30% within 18 months. | Reduce total weight by 15% within 18 months. Identify areas to replace foods with healthier choices. | Weight management programs, support groups. Initiate daily lunchti me walking groups. Appraise vending food and beverage machine selections. |
| Create a happy and supportive work environment. | Reduce the number of stressed employees by 20% within 6 months. Identify short and long term stressors. | Show prompt appreciation to employees. Offer weekly onsite yoga/meditation classes. Provide financial counseling. Sleep management course. Time-management course. Have a weekly comedy DVD during Friday lunchtime. Survey to determine short and long term stressors. Introduce flexi-time. Develop and implement policies to support flexi-time. |

# S.M.A.R.T. INTERVENTIONS

| GOAL<br>With W's | OBJECTIVE<br>With W's | INTERVENTION<br>With W's |
|---|---|---|
| | | |
| | | |
| | | |

# WELLNESS TEAM SKILLS-SET

| DEPARTMENT | SKILLS |
|---|---|
| Executive | Final decision-making, authorization, endorsement, and approval of resource requests. |
| HR | Compliance, health and safety, insurance, demographic knowledge. |
| Benefits | Sourcing free resources from vendors. Explaining benefits changes via monthly e-newsletter. |
| Marketing | Branding and promotion of wellness message. |
| Catering | Healthier food and meal choices. |
| Finance | Budgeting and ROI calculation. |
| IT | Deliver health messages using intranet and apps. Data protection. |
| Wellness Champion | Supports the wellness initiative. From any department and level of authority. Is a campaigner and advocate. |
|  |  |
|  |  |

# EXTRINSIC INCENTIVES EXAMPLE

| EXTRINSIC REWARD | VALUE | DISADVANTAGE |
|---|---|---|
| Payment of program or gym fees. | Given at completion of an exercise program or annual gym membership. | Reduced motivation due to length of duration between starting and completing program. |
| Merchandise. Hats, T-shirts, mugs etc. | Wellness program branding, inexpensive, suitable for team-building. | Limited ongoing use, low visibility. |
| Elite Services. | Pampering and privileged access to events and luxury activities. Can be low cost if a donated service or pass. | Limited use if only for one person, rather than offering two passes. |
| Waiver of pre-existing condition. | Linked to the Health plan. | The initial value to the employee may decline over time. |
| Bonus for Medical Savings account. | Useful for anticipated medical expenses. | May not be fully utilized. It is a one-off payment. |
| Time off. | Generally | Value diminishes |

| | | |
|---|---|---|
| Immediate. | popular. Can be used to suit employees' personal needs. Non-taxable. | on whether employee is part or full-time and amount of vacation time allowed. |
| Time off. Delayed. | Generally popular. Can be used to suit employees' personal needs. Non-taxable. | Demotivating due to length of time between reward and taking time off. |
| Gift Cards. | A popular reward. | Taxable income. |
| Cash. Immediate. | Highest incentive. | Taxable income therefore cash-in-hand is less. |
| Cash. At end of intervention. | Opportunity to have a higher monetary reward than immediate cash. | Can lose interest, as reward is too distant. Taxable income therefore cash-in-hand is less. |

# INTRINSIC INCENTIVES EXAMPLE

| INTRINSIC REWARD | VALUE | DISADVANTAGE |
|---|---|---|
| Recognition. | Low cost with photographs, certificates, and company-wide email. Motivates other employees. | Limited use in small companies. Must vary the individuals or teams who are recognized. |
| Community Player. | Membership of an exclusive club. Clothing that shows belonging to special group. | Not of value to every employee. May disincentivize or alienate some employees. |
| President's Club Resort Conference attendee with management. | High-profile. Usually abroad in a luxury hotel. Partner is often invited. | Reward may lessen if partner is not included. May be intimidating for some employees. |
| Advanced training or certification in a skill the employee wishes to enhance. | This can be a personal, creative, or health skill or it can be a work-related skill such as training in public speaking. | Can be challenging to complete creating an adverse reaction to further participation. |
| Volunteering. | Low-cost, creates positive energy regarding self and organization. | Can involve large numbers of employees and thus challenging to organize. |

# WORKSITE WELLNESS COMMITTEE

| | Name of Member | Department | Wellness Role | Date Joined Committee |
|---|---|---|---|---|
| 1. | | | | |
| 2. | | | | |
| 3. | | | | |
| 4. | | | | |
| 5. | | | | |
| 6. | | | | |
| 7. | | | | |
| 8. | | | | |
| 9. | | | | |
| 10. | | | | |

# EMPLOYEE INTEREST SURVEY

## Sample Questions

To be used on-line with questions and response ranges such as:

- Indicate your interest for each of the following:
- Very Interested, Somewhat Interested, Not Interested.

- Indicate how likely you would participate in the following health promotion programs:
- Extremely Likely, Somewhat Likely, Unlikely.

- I am interested in participating in the following programs:
- Strongly Agree, Agree, Neither Agree Nor Disagree, Disagree, Strongly Disagree.

To determine the preferred time of day to participate in wellness programs:

| Time of day | Extremely Likely | Somewhat Likely | Unlikely |
|---|---|---|---|
| Before work | | | |
| During meetings | | | |
| During work day | | | |
| During lunch | | | |
| After work | | | |
| Activities lasting 30-60 minutes | | | |
| Activities lasting longer than one | | | |

| hour | | | |
|------|------|------|------|
| During weekends | | | |

## General Questions

- Indicate your interest for each of the following:
- Very Interested, Somewhat Interested, Not Interested.

1. Participating regularly in a wellness program
2. Group activities
3. Personal activities
4. Time management skills
5. Financial wellness
6. Stress management
7. Relaxation techniques
8. Sleep disorders
9. Communication skills
10. Social events with co-workers
11. Tobacco cessation
12. Alcohol use
13. Ergonomic evaluation of work station
14. Weekly games or movie during Friday lunch
15. Participating in onsite screenings.
16. Eldercare
17. Parenting skills
18. Auto-safety
19. Other

## Health Program Questions

- Indicate your interest for each of the following:

- Very Interested, Somewhat Interested, Not Interested.

1. Skin cancer prevention
2. Blood pressure management
3. Pregnancy and lactation programs
4. Heart disease prevention
5. Type II Diabetes prevention or management
6. Depression
7. Arthritis prevention or management
8. Foot care
9. Other

## Nutrition Program Questions

- Indicate your interest for each of the following:
- Very Interested, Somewhat Interested, Not Interested.

1. Nutrition education programs
2. Healthier food choices in a restaurant
3. Cooking lessons
4. Healthy recipes
5. Tasting events of foods and beverages
6. Incorporating more fruits and vegetables into my daily diet
7. Weight management program
8. Weight loss challenge
9. Onsite vending with healthier snacks and beverages
10. Decreasing the amount of candy & sweets I eat each day.
11. Other

## Physical Program Questions

- Indicate your interest for each of the following:
- Very Interested, Somewhat Interested, Not Interested.

1. Physical education programs
2. Increasing my physical activity levels
3. How to incorporate daily physical activity into my personal time
4. Adding physical activities during work hours
5. Yoga classes
6. Walking club
7. Running club
8. Cycling club
9. Other sports league
10. Strength training
11. Fitness challenges
12. Avoiding sports injuries
13. Other

## Tobacco Cessation Questions

- Indicate your interest for each of the following:
- Very Interested, Somewhat Interested, Not Interested.

1. I want to reduce second-hand smoke in my workplace
2. If you smoke, do you want to quit?
3. I want to attend information sessions or classes about quitting tobacco use.
4. I want to attend sessions during work time
5. I want to attend sessions during my lunch break
6. I want to attend sessions before work
7. I want to attend sessions after work
8. Other

## Incentives Questions

- Indicate how likely these items will motivate you to participate in our wellness program.
- Extremely Likely, Somewhat Likely, Unlikely.

## Types of Incentives

1. Cash
2. Gym membership
3. Mall gift cards
4. Movie tickets
5. Music gift cards
6. Management recognition
7. Workout clothing
8. Workout bags, mats, water bottles
9. Workout equipment, tools
10. Massage treatments

11. Electronic wearables, pedometers, watches
12. Prize drawing for seasonal items
13. Paid time off
14. Other

## General Questions Using Another Format

- Indicate your interest for each of the following:
- Strongly Agree, Agree, Neither Agree Nor Disagree, Disagree, Strongly Disagree.

1. Executives at (name of company) care about the health of the employees.
2. Having a wellness program is a benefit.
3. My co-workers support my health activities.
4. My manager supports my health activities.
5. (Name of company) is a healthy place to work.
6. Other

# WELLNESS PROGRAM EVALUATION SURVEY

This type of survey can be used to determine the opinion of employees to the overall wellness program, rather than to one specific program or intervention.

- Use the same approach to the evaluation survey as you would with an employee information survey.
- Structure the questions so that they remain unidentifiable.
- Remind employees that the survey is anonymous.

**Response Ranges Include:**

- Very Interested, Somewhat Interested, Not Interested.
- Strongly Agree, Agree, Neither Agree Nor Disagree, Disagree, Strongly Disagree.
- Extremely Likely, Somewhat Likely, Unlikely.
- Yes, No.

**Demographics:**

Ensure that the age range is appropriate for your organization and that there is a wide representation of both sexes to avoid any possible identification of respondents.

- Male, Female
- Age Group: Under 35, 36-45, 46-55, 56-65, 66 and older. (Alter the range to suit your organization.)

## Sample Questions

- Please indicate your level of satisfaction using this scale:
- Yes, No

1. Are you aware that (name of company) has a wellness program?
2. Is wellness important to you?
3. Has management been supportive of the program?
4. Have you participated in the program?
5. Did it help you to make better wellness choices? If yes, please indicate in which of the following areas:

| Tobacco cessation | Physical activity | Healthier nutrition |
|---|---|---|
| Stress management | Weight loss | Sleep disorders |
| Other: | | |

6. Does the program meet your wellness goals?
7. Would you participate in future programs?
8. Would recommend the program to your colleagues?

In what way could the program be more effective?

|  |
|--|
|  |

Thank you for your participation.

Please return this survey to:

_____

by this date:

_____

# PARTICIPATION EVALUATION SURVEY

Name of Program:

_____

Name of Presenter:

_____

Date: _____

Please take a minute to complete this evaluation. Your feedback is very important to us. On a scale of 1-5, please rate the following with 5 being the highest.

| | 5 | 4 | 3 | 2 | 1 |
|---|---|---|---|---|---|
| The time of the presentation was convenient for you. | | | | | |
| What was your overall rating of the presenter? | | | | | |
| The information was well presented. | | | | | |
| Your overall experience during this program was positive. | | | | | |
| The program has helped me to make healthier choices. | | | | | |
| You would participate in this program again? | | | | | |
| The information was useful to you? | | | | | |
| You would recommend this program to another employee. | | | | | |

What did you enjoy the most about this presentation?

| |
|---|
| |

What topics would you like to see in future presentations?

| |
|---|
| |

Thank you for your participation.

Please return this survey to: _____

by this date: _____

# PHYSICAL PROGRAM EVALUATION

Program Name:

_____

Program Leader:

_____

Date: _____

Please take a minute to complete this evaluation. Your feedback is very important to us. On a scale of 1-5, please rate the following with 5 being the highest.

|  | 5 | 4 | 3 | 2 | 1 |
|---|---|---|---|---|---|
| Was the time of the program convenient for you? |  |  |  |  |  |
| Was the information presented easily understandable? |  |  |  |  |  |
| The wellness program was beneficial to me. |  |  |  |  |  |
| I enjoy being physically active. |  |  |  |  |  |
| I am physically active three or more days a week. |  |  |  |  |  |
| I am physically active five or more days a week. |  |  |  |  |  |
| I consider physical activity to be a high priority in my daily life. |  |  |  |  |  |
| I drink at least 8 glasses of water a day. |  |  |  |  |  |
| I feel happy. |  |  |  |  |  |

| | | | | | |
|---|---|---|---|---|---|
| The program resources are helping me to attain my fitness goals. | | | | | |
| I have support from my co-workers. | | | | | |
| I have support from my family. | | | | | |
| The program objectives were met. | | | | | |

What did you enjoy the most about this program?

What topics would you like to see in future program?

Thank you for your participation.

Please return this survey to: _____

by this  date: _____

# POINTS INCENTIVE PROGRAM

**Employee Name:** _____

**Duration**_____

**Start:** _____

**End** _____

| DATE | ACTIVITY | POINTS ALLOCATED | POINTS EARNED |
|------|----------|------------------|---------------|
|      |          |                  |               |
|      |          |                  |               |
|      |          |                  |               |
|      |          |                  |               |
|      |          |                  |               |
|      |          |                  |               |
|      |          |                  |               |
|      |          |                  |               |
|      |          |                  |               |
|      |          |                  |               |
|      |          |                  |               |
|      |          |                  |               |
|      |          |                  |               |
|      | TOTAL    |                  |               |

Points Converted To:

_____ Award

_____ Award

_____ Award

Made in the USA
Columbia, SC
17 May 2021

38090741R00134